And There Was Light

בְּרֵאשִׁית בָּרָא אֱלֹהִים אֵת
הַשָּׁמַיִם וְאֵת הָאָרֶץ׃ וְהָאָרֶץ
הָיְתָה תֹהוּ וָבֹהוּ וְחֹשֶׁךְ עַל־פְּנֵי
תְהוֹם וְרוּחַ אֱלֹהִים מְרַחֶפֶת עַל־
פְּנֵי הַמָּיִם׃ וַיֹּאמֶר אֱלֹהִים יְהִי אוֹר
וַיְהִי־אוֹר׃ וַיַּרְא אֱלֹהִים אֶת־הָאוֹר
כִּי־טוֹב וַיַּבְדֵּל אֱלֹהִים בֵּין הָאוֹר וּבֵין
הַחֹשֶׁךְ׃ וַיִּקְרָא אֱלֹהִים לָאוֹר יוֹם
וְלַחֹשֶׁךְ קָרָא לָיְלָה וַיְהִי־עֶרֶב וַיְהִי־
בֹקֶר יוֹם אֶחָד׃

From the **First Book of Moses: Genesis**, Chapter 1, Verses 1–5:

In the beginning God created the heaven and the earth.
And the earth was without form, and void;
And darkness was upon the face of the deep
And the Spirit of God moved upon the face of the waters.
And God said, Let there be Light: and there was Light.
And God saw the Light, that it was good:
And God divided the Light from the Darkness.
And God called the light Day, and the darkness He called Night.
And the evening and the morning were the first day.

And There Was Light

From the Creation of the World to Noah's Ark

by

Jakob Streit

Translated by Ekkehard Piening
Illustrations by Assja Turgenieff

Printed with support from the Waldorf Curriculum Fund

Published by:
Waldorf Publications at the
Research Institute for Waldorf Education
351 Fairview Avenue, Suite 625
Hudson, NY 12534

Title: **And There Was Light**
Author: Jakob Streit
Translator: Ekkehard Piening
Illustrator: Assja Turgenieff
Editor: David Mitchell
Proofreader: Ann Erwin
Cover: David Mitchell

Completely revised and re-edited
ISBN # 1-888365-74-9
Last printed in 1976 by Walter Keller Press
Dornach, CH-4143, Switzerland

Contents

The Seven Days of Creation

The World's Beginning 7
Michael and the Dragon 11
The First Day of Creation 13
The Second Day 15
The Third Day 15
The Fourth Day 17
Edelweiss and the Mountain-Flowers 19
Something about Poisonous Plants 20
Why Roses Have Thorns 21
The Fifth Day 21
The Sixth Day 24
The Dove and the Lamb 27
The Creation of Man 28
The Seventh Day 29
In Paradise 31
The Fall 32
On Earth 34

The Sons of Cain

Cain and Abel 35
What Cain and Abel Dreamed 37
Cain Conquers the Wolf 37
When Eve Wept 39
How Cain Slew Abel 41
Adam Buries Abel in the First Grave on Earth 43
Seth, the New Brother of Cain 44
An Angel Reveals the Book of Life to Adam 45
Adam's Death 46
The Sons of Cain 49
Jabal, the Tamer of the Animals 49
Jubal Brings Music to Humankind 57
Thubal-Cain, the Inventor and Smith 58
The Sons of Cain and the First Houses 60
The Three Knives 65
Jubal Makes Music for the Animals 66
Jubal Plays for Men 68

Of Wicked Companions and Their Evil Deeds 69
Kenos in the Forest Cave........ 71
How Jubal Escapes Great Danger 73
The Death of Seth........ 75
How Enos Brought the Worship of Idols to Humankind 76
Through Enoch the Light of Goodness Returns to Earth........ 77
Enoch Makes His First Offering 78
Enoch Finds the Cave of the Holy Book 80
Enoch's Wanderings........ 80
The Mountain of God and Its Priests 82
Enoch's Ascension into Heaven 83

Noah's Ark

Old Methusala 86
Where Is the House of the Righteous?........ 87
Noah's Birth 88
The Child Noah's Anger........ 88
The City of a Hundred Idols........ 90
The Command 92
The King with the Black Crown........ 92
Raphael Guides Noah to the Book of Life........ 94
The Commandment to Build the Ark 95
Sem, Ham, Jafet, and the Animals 96
Will the Ark Be Destroyed? 96
Gathering the Animals........ 98
Entering the Ark........ 99
Adam's Casket 101
The Ark Is Sealed and the Rain Begins to Fall 101
The Flood 102
Distress in the Ark........ 104
Raven-Flight and Dove-Message 105
The New World 106
The Offering of Thanks........ 107
The Devil in Noah's Vines........ 107
Sem and the Angels 108

Afterword........ 109
Translator's Note / Editor's Note 110
For Recitation: Genesis, Chapter 1, Verses 1–5 111

The Seven Days of Creation

The World's Beginning

Long ago there was no earth. There were no clouds and no stars, no, not even a sun! Darkness was everywhere. No animals bounded and no birds flew. How could they have, since there was no earth? Did anything exist at all? There was a heaven, an upper world, high above our stars. In heaven, God's eye shone like a sun. Small angels could not look directly into God Father's shining eye, for it was much too bright. It shone more brightly than our sun and would have blinded them. The great angels, however, could look for a moment into God Father's eye. They could even come near His throne when they wanted to tell Him something. All heaven rang with beautiful music. Flutes, violins, and harps resounded, and angels sang long songs. Whenever one concert came to an end, a new one would begin. Some angels sewed golden stars upon God Father's mantle of blue, while others caught lightbeams and kneaded them into precious stones. All was splendor and a great wonder.

Once two great angels knelt in prayer before God Father's throne. As they rose they flew together downwards through the heavens, for God's throne stood high and steep like the peak of a mountain. All at once one of the angels, who was named Lucifer, stood still. He gazed upon the splendor of heaven and upon his own shining garment and thought to himself, "How nice it is, to be such a God. My garment is almost as bright as that of God Father! Indeed, it is bright enough that I might sit in God's place!" As Lucifer thought this, a wispy, grey cloud gently hovered before his forehead.

It floated toward his heart and there made a spot upon his garment. Lucifer was frightened when he saw this and quickly covered the spot with his wing. As he went on his way through heaven, he met Michael. Michael asked, "Lucifer, what is wrong? Are you ill? You have a spot upon your garment!"

"My heart aches a little, that's all," Lucifer answered. He quickly flew to the lesser angels and said to them, "Make a fiery red mantle for me. I must cover something." They made the mantle, and when he put it on, the spot could no longer be seen.

Lucifer stayed with the lesser angels and asked them, "Will you help me build a throne? I will sit upon it and be your god. You are not permitted to go to the highest throne, but to my throne you may always come." Many angels were frightened at these words. Others, however, liked Lucifer so much that they agreed. These angels ceased singing and making music. They also ceased sewing stars upon God Father's mantle.

Now Michael saw what Lucifer was doing. Full of dread, he brought the news to God Father that Lucifer was building a throne for himself. God Father spoke, "Tell Lucifer to destroy his heart. I will give him a new, shining heart. If he will do so, bring him to me. If he will not do so, he shall have his throne, but not in heaven! If he refuses to heed my words, take your sword and cast him out of heaven." Thus God Father spoke.

All this Michael told Lucifer. But Lucifer had stirred up many angels; he did not want a new heart. The angels ceased singing. Loud voices shouted in confusion. Thunder rumbled through heaven and a fiery wind blew. Michael took up his sword. Bolts of lightning flashed from it. He called out with a mighty voice, "All those who will be true to God stand by my side."

Lucifer shouted, "Those who would go with me into the new heaven, stand by my side!" Thus the spirits separated into two groups. Michael's group was above, Lucifer's below.

Now Michael struck against the wall of heaven with his lightning sword. Loud crashes resounded, and a deep gash appeared. Lucifer and his angels fought desperately, for they did not want to go into the darkness below. But God Father's light no longer shone upon them. The beautiful colors in their garments and wings paled and faded. Their faces became gloomy and ugly. Claws grew out of their fingers. They howled and wailed but were forced to give way before Michael and his hosts. Lucifer and his followers were cast from heaven. They plunged down to the deep, dark depths.

Since that time there exists a dark, lower world. The evil spirits made a small fire out of their own light, for they were cold. They danced around it and it grew into a huge fire. They forged a throne for Lucifer and placed it upon the fire that he should always be warm. Michael closed the cleft in heaven. A scar remained where it had been.

Michael and the Dragon

The evil spirits spoke to one another, "Let us make a dragon and ride into heaven upon it! With mighty jaws and teeth, it shall tear open the wall of heaven." In the dark depths, they created a dragon. They hammered and polished thousands of sharp scales for its body. Its tongue was like a fiery flame, its wings like those of bats. When it was finished, the dragon had no soul.

Then one evil spirit cried out, "I will be its soul," and immediately slipped into the monster.

The others shouted, "Go!" and the dragon flew up toward the scar in heaven's wall. The evil spirits rode upon its back or followed behind.

At this time, many angels were gathered around God Father's throne. They were singing and making music. All at once there was a loud scratching. A whistling and howling disturbed the angels' singing. Michael saw the ugly dragon; it was trying to gnaw through heaven's wall. A host of evil spirits sat upon the monster. With both of his hands, Michael then took light from God Father's throne and dipped his sword into this light.

When he came to the scar, a huge paw with hideous claws and the scaly horns of the dragon's head were already visible. Lightning flashed from Michael's sword. Forcing the dragon under his feet, Michael thrust him through with his sword. The evil spirits fluttered forth like bats. The dragon plunged to the depths and coughed his last. His soul crawled out and whined pitifully. Michael called into the depths, "You evil spirits! Remain below! Perhaps in future times God Father will give you opportunity to make good what you have done."

The evil spirits growled and then fell silent, for God Father had opened heaven's gate. He spoke, "You spirits of the deep! You wanted to found your own dominion! Now you have it and you must remain below. Will you obey me?"

Through gnashing teeth they answered, "Yes." Then heaven's gate closed. Thus there remained an upper and a lower world.

The First Day of Creation

As God Father sat upon his throne, he called out seven words through heaven. The seven colors of the rainbow appeared and shone in seven circles around his throne. The angels were astounded at the mighty, beautiful light.

The archangel Raphael spoke, "Shall we weave a mantle for God Father from the seven colors?"

The archangel Gabriel answered, "Perhaps a new hall shall be built of the light!"

Oriphiel said, "The colors could be seven steps to God's throne."

Archangel Michael stood silently, waiting for God Father's sign, which would show what was to be done.

Then something wonderful happened. Behind the rainbow, majestic fire angels lifted a great cloud curtain, revealing a hall of heaven that had never been seen before. In the hallway were thousands upon thousands of sleeping souls, as countless as the stars in heaven. And God spoke to the angels, "These are sleeping human souls. Would you like to help create a middle world where they can awaken and live?"

The angels answered with a jubilant, "Yes!"

The fire-angels lowered the curtain and opened the gate of heaven. Outside it was cold and dark, waste and void. Then God Father spoke, that his voice resounded through the darkness, "Let there be Light!"

Light began to shine, to blaze and to sparkle brightly. The darkness withdrew to the depths. Fire-angels stripped flames from their garments, and the new world grew warm. It bubbled and flamed and flashed. Thunder rumbled and rolled so loudly that the evil spirits in the deep huddled in fear. Above them the angels' eyes, like a thousand suns, sparkled from the bright light of the first day of creation.

The Second Day

On the second day God Father said, "Let us create the air!" for there was, as yet, no air in the world. The air-angels encircled God Father. They began to blow and move their powerful wings. But when the air fanned the glowing earth fire, it flickered and flashed. Huge fire storms burst forth. They whirled high and low and raged in wild confusion. Many angels were pulled along by the twisting, whirling streams of air and were in great need of help. Then a multitude of light, nimble angels came, and pushed downward all that was heavy. Below it was now like an ocean of fire, above, like an ocean of air and light. Thus an above and a below came about in the world. But the human souls behind the cloud-curtain still did not know that a new world was being created for them. They still slept soundly.

The Third Day

In the airy, fiery world, the wind blew great whirling fire storms upward. "Let us cool the world," said the angels. With God's help, they created water, and it flowed into the world.

From the flames voices called, "Water, we will boil you!" And there was tremendous bubbling, and boiling and hissing.

God Father said, "The water shall be by itself, and the fire also!" The angels caused the water to rush to the depths and the fiery light to the heights. In the depths the waters gathered and became the sea. Under the sea, solid ground formed. This was the first soil, but it was under the water.

And God said, "Let green plants be created!" The plant-angels came and created the first green plants in the water. As the plants grew out of the dark bottom, they longed for the light. They grew higher and higher, finally reaching the surface of the water. One angel saw the green stems growing out of the water. He caught heavenly light and formed a white crown. He placed this upon the top of the stem. This became the waterlily.

As the angel was creating this wondrous blossom, a flaming fire-angel flew by. Quickly the water-lily angel covered the blossom with his wing, that the heat might not burn it. The fire-angel called, "What are you hiding? Here nothing may be hidden. It may not be!"

"I fear you will burn it if I show it to you," said the plant-angel.

"No, I will burn nothing of beauty. Ah," the fireangel exclaimed, "Such a beautiful starry crown! The fire shall not harm it." Not long thereafter, many such blossoms adorned the sea.

The plant-angel thought, "If there were only firm soil above the water, then a glorious earth-garden could be planted." He flew upward to God Father's throne.

Majestic angels guarded the throne and lightning flashed from their garments. One of them called out in a thunderous voice, "What does a plant-angel seek here?"

"I must ask God Father something. I do not know how to continue my work on earth," the plant-angel replied. They let him pass. The plant-angel asked, "Can you, God Father, raise the soil out of the water? We plant-angels would like to let herbs and flowers grow into the air."

And God said, "You think my thoughts. It shall be so." With His right hand he pressed deep into the ocean. At each side, hills and mountains arose, as well as brooks and streams. And out of God Father's Word, the plant-angels created herbs, flowers, and the trees of the earth.

The Fourth Day

The fallen angels of the depths noticed that above them something new was being created. Again and again great crashing and rumbling resounded from the middle world. "What are they doing up there?" they asked one another. Lucifer sent out messengers, but these could not come close to the fiery, glowing world because the light caused them pain. From a distance, they could see sparkling, as of star flowers and miniature suns. Lights flashed and dimmed in a majestic play of colors.

All this the messengers reported to Lucifer, who said to himself, "Perhaps later we, too, can help build this world and show what we can do."

At that time the brilliant light of the sun and the stars was still within the earth. Often storms and fiery whirlwinds blew. The plants could not thrive and grow peacefully.

Then God said, "Shine forth, O lights in the Firmament!" The great light-angels gathered together the fiery brightness of the world until they had formed a huge sun. With one mighty thrust, they carried the sun into the sky. The light that the smaller angels gathered was kneaded into stars. These, too, were lifted into the heavens. Then, with a mighty gesture, God Father set the sun into motion. Another motion set the stars upon their paths. Thus their heavenly course began, and since that time there is day and night. That is how it came to be cooler on the earth. The plants were able to grow unhindered by heat or whirlwinds. There was order among them. They grasped the firm ground with their roots. Henceforth, the flowers looked upward to the sun and the stars. They faced the shining light, knowing the sun to be their mother and the stars their brothers and sisters. Every flower has its star in the heavens.

The earth, however, grew colder and colder. The soil became hard. Many angels said, "If this should continue, soon no more plants will grow."

Then God said, "Take from the earth all that is hard, firm and cold. We will create another heavenly light, the moon." The angels fulfilled God's Word and with His strength, they lifted the moon out of the earth and set it in the heavens. This was the last heavenly light to be created. The sun gives the earth light and warmth, bringing life to all things upon it. The moon is a cold, lifeless world that causes the earth to harden ever more.

Edelweiss and the Mountain-Flowers

At the end of the fourth day of creation, God Father looked upon the earth from a heavenly cloud. Many angels were at his side. He saw the green and flowering plants, and He praised the angels who had helped to cover the earth with such a beautiful garment. The cloud floated towards the mountains, but there, the meadows, flowers and trees did not grow so well. In the mountains only low shrubs and herbs, as well as cold, hard rocks could be found. Then the younger angels cried, "God Father, may we go to earth once more and create flowers here also?"

God answered, "Go forth and continue weaving the earth's garment."

When the host of young angels reached the rocky mountains, daylight was fading. The sun had nearly set. "We cannot create any green," one angel cried. "Without sunlight, it is not possible." In the evening sky, they beheld the pale glow of the stars and said, "Let us create flowers of starlight." Delicate hands guided the starlight earthward. Silvery leaves budded forth and arranged themselves into star-shapes. In this way, the edelweiss came into being.

When the light blue sky shone over the mountains the next morning, the angels created gentian, and to this day gentian is sky blue. From the red of the sunrise and sunset they made the alpine rose.

Something about Poisonous Plants

The sun spoke to the flowers, "Open wide your cups in the daytime that you may drink my light. And close them at night. The good moon and the stars will keep watch. But when dense clouds hide moon and stars and no ray of light shines, then never open your cups, lest harm befall you. The spirits of darkness seek to bring evil into the light of creation."

On a pitch-dark night, a shadowy being flitted over the earth. This evil being sought to bring harm to the plants. Coming to a forest flower, it whispered with a false voice, "Poor forest flower, how tiny you are. Open your blossom that I may blow into it. Then you will grow tall, and you will bloom majestically." The forest flower remained tightly dosed. The devil whispered, "Open up. It is night-time and no one will see. I will cover you with my wings." Slowly the flower opened its cup. All at once, the devil spat into the blossom! O, the pain! The plant shuddered and all the petals fell upon the ground as if they had been burned. The evil spirit laughed gleefully and sped away.

The next morning the dew-angels came, bringing refreshing dew to field and wood. One of them came to the forest flower and was aghast at what he saw. "Forest flower, what has happened?"

"O, pull me up by the roots! Tear me out!" cried the flower. "I did not heed the sun's advice, and opened my cup in the darkness of night. I have been spoiled and suffer burning pain."

The angel caressed its leaves and said, "I will not pull you up. Draw all the burning juice together into a berry. Hold the sap gathered therein. Perhaps some day it will be of use." And so it happened. Today this forest flower is called the deadly nightshade. It blooms with white petals. Its berries are purple-black and poisonous when eaten, but they can be made into healing medicine.

Why Roses Have Thorns

On another night, an evil spirit scurried about and came to a rose bush. One beautiful red rose was in bloom. In the evening the rose had closed its petals, but its fragrance still perfumed the night air. This fragrance irritated the fallen spirit so much that he was forced to sneeze thoroughly several times. He scolded, "How this flower stinks; I'd like to tear it apart with my claws!" Then he held his breath, came close to the blossom and whispered, "O rose, open your petals. I will breathe upon you and you shall have a sweeter fragrance!" The rose remained silent, with its petals tightly dosed. The evil one whispered again, "Rose, open your petals. I will breathe on you and you shall grow into a mighty tree. If not, you will always remain a little shrub." Still the rose kept its petals tightly closed. Then all at once, the spirit grew angry and tore at the rose's stem with his claws. He shook and rattled the stem furiously. When he saw that he could not succeed in doing more harm, he disappeared.

The rose suffered terrible pain where the stem had been torn by the devil's claws. Day came. The wounds healed, but there were scars which grew into spiky thorns. A passing light-angel said to the rose, "Rejoice in your spiky thorns. They are a remembrance of your steadfastness." Since that time, roses have thorns.

The Fifth Day

And God said, "It is so quiet on earth. Let us create animals." He called into the sea, "Fishes in the water, take on life!" In the depths of the sea, life began to stir. First the angels created the shellfish on the bottom. They joined two shells together and let something live between them. These were the clams, which slept and slept on the bottom of the sea. The angels continued molding and forming. They

created creatures with small water wings and silvery scales; these were the fish. They were given no eyelids, and to this day they sleep with open eyes. Larger and larger fish were created. The sharks, whales and the dolphins appeared. Many leaped into the air, only to dive down into the water again. Glittering goldfish, rainbow trout, and many other wondrous colored fish could be seen shimmering through the waters.

And God called into the air, "Birds, fly and jubilate in the air!" Then the angels created the 'air-fish.' The bodies were smaller and the wings bigger than those of the water-fish. Instead of scales, there were soft, colorful feathers. The fish in the water looked up to the birds and said, "We, too, want to fly," and made great leaps out of the water.

Some birds looked down at the fishes and said, "We can swim," and settled upon the water. These were the geese, ducks, and swans. Swallows built their nests in rocks and trees, and titmice built theirs in the bushes.

A sparrow said to the fishes, "We are faster than you and we work harder. We build nests, lay eggs and hatch them. Then cheep-cheep, and the eggs hatch!"

But the fish were content to be fish. One fish said to a sparrow as it was drinking water, "Water carries better than air. You must always flap and flutter or you will fall. When we fish compress our belly, which holds our swim bladder, down we go. If we relax, up we go!"

In the glittering morning sunlight, when the birds rose up into the air, they could hear God's angels singing and making music. They tried to sing the heavenly songs and jubilate like the angels. That is how the birds learned to sing. Many have forgotten their songs except for a few notes: cheep-cheep or too-whit, too-whit. Those that avoided flying into the sunlight sang caw-caw or whoo-whoo! And so passed the fifth day.

The Sixth Day

When the dew-angels came to the meadow the next morning, they asked the flowers why they were so sad. The flowers answered, "The birds take no notice of us at all. They do not visit us but merely go rushing by. We are rooted to the ground and can only sway gently in the wind."

The dew-angels reported this to God Father. God Father made them a gift of a many-colored cloud and said, "Take it to earth and there lift the cloud's veil." The dew-angels took the cloud to earth. High in the air they lifted the veil and out fluttered many thousands of butterflies.

When the flowers saw this, they rejoiced and said to each other, "Look! Angel children! See the little heavenly brothers. Their wings are like petals." The blossoms seemed to draw them near. The butterflies fluttered to the blossoms. Caressing the blossoms, they asked for honey. The flowers gladly gave them sweet nectar. The butterflies in turn told the flowers about the miracles of heaven.

In the woodlands and amid the grasses, there were many flowers which the butterflies could not reach. These plants spoke of their loneliness to the dew-angels. "The butterflies do not come to us. We are forsaken and alone." God Father, therefore, made a gift of another heavenly cloud, which was somewhat brown in color. When the veil was pulled away, swarms of buzzing bees flew out and scattered over the earth. The queen bees, however, sat each upon a branch and whistled softly. Although the whistling sound of the queens was faint, each family of bees gathered around its queen. They sought homes in hollow trees or in the ground and there built their hives. From that day on, even the smallest, most hidden flowers had visitors.

A bee and a butterfly once chanced to meet upon a blossom. With compassion the butterfly said to the bee, "Did God Father have no more colors left for you?" You are as brown as wood, and your wings are so pitifully small. How can you fly with them?"

The bee smiled and said, "Do you see the tiny forget-me-not in the grass? Fly to it and back. I will wait." O woe! The butterfly caught his wings in the grass and the bee had to help free him. The bee said, "Fly with me to the lindentree." But when the butterfly arrived, the bee had already been there and gone. The bee laughed and said, "Dear butterfly, your colors are beautiful and your wings magnificent. But have you understood that you need not pity me? God Father has wisely ordered everything." The butterfly felt ashamed for having boasted about his colorful wings.

But what about the bumble-bee and her heavy fur coat? She can fly even in cold weather. When she bumps into things, she is protected and cushioned.

And God Father spoke to the earth, "Earth, your land shall be alive with animals of every kind!" And together with the angels, He created the animals of the earth. The frog lived like a fish in the water. They gave him feet. He lost his tail, hopped onto shore and croaked. Another animal was given a slender shape and quick feet – the lizard. One was given a cover for its back – the turtle. Another carried its house on its back, but had no feet – the snail. One lived in the hills and meadows, dug holes in the ground and sat up – the groundhog.

The mountain said, "I would like to have animals on my rocks." The ibex and mountain goat were created and came to live there.

The forest said, "I would like to be home to many kinds of animals. In me they may dig holes and build nests." There were squirrels, deer, rabbits, and foxes.

Who was to eat the plentiful grass? Cows, sheep, horses, and goats. The bulls tested their strength by locking horns. Fiery-eyed horses raced over the plains neighing loudly, as their manes whipped in the wind. And so creatures came to live all over the earth.

Before God Father created the animals, He held in His mind an image of man. In every new animal that was created, the angels came closer to creating this image. And so it is that many animals also have five fingers or five claws. Some of them, such as the squirrel, the bear, the ape, and the groundhog, strive to walk upright like man. Every animal in some way resembles man.

The Dove and the Lamb

One day an evil spirit saw a snow-white dove sitting upon a tree. He was annoyed at its white feathers. He called and coaxed, "My pretty dove, come fly to me!"

Ri-coo, ri-coo,
I don't like you!

The evil spirit called again, "Come, my dove, I'll paint you with many colors, that you won't be such a boring white." He crept up to the tree and was about to climb it when the dove spread its wings and flew away. Angrily he shook the tree upon which the dove had been sitting, but he could do the dove no harm.

Evening came. The sun sank behind the mountains and most animals went to sleep. Only a pert little mouse crept about in the darkness. When the evil spirit spied the mouse, he seized her and said, "Now I, too, will make a bird." He tugged at the mouse's ears and legs until he stretched them. Then he tore off a piece of his skin and fixed it on the mouse's back. He also fixed the legs and tail to the skin. All night the mouse fluttered fearfully to and fro.

When morning came, she crept into the darkest corner of a hollow tree. She was ashamed to fly in the light when the other birds sang. Thus the bat came to be a night-creature and has remained so ever since.

Another time, the evil spirit saw a lamb in the meadow. He tried to lure it toward him, but the lamb shied away from him. The evil one whispered in a disguised voice, "If you let me comb your wool with a golden comb, all your wool will turn to gold!" But the lamb sprang away.

Angrily the evil spirit disappeared into the woods. There he met a dog searching for food. He brought forth a chunk of devil's bread and fed it to the dog. When the dog had swallowed it greedily, he began to howl loudly. He felt such a burning pain in his belly that all his hackles rose. This creature became the wolf. The evil spirit chased him out of the wood into the meadow among the lambs. The wolf fell upon the herd and seized the lamb that had run from the evil spirit. Only with blood can the wolf still the pain in his belly.

The Creation of Man

God Father gazed upon the earth and said to the angels, "Let us create man!" And the angels brought something of all that was upon the earth. The rocks were made into bones, the rivers into blood, the stars into eyes, the soil into the body, and the wind yielded breath. And God formed the head round as the moon, and the arms, legs and fingers like rays of light. As the sun in the heavens warms and nourishes all life, so He gave man a heart to sustain him.

When the body of man had been created, a great angel brought forth a sleeping soul from behind the cloud curtain and placed it into God's Hand. Then God Father, with His living breath, breathed the soul into man. The angels of heaven came and beheld the great wonder. Man had been created! His name was Adam, which means "son of earth." He was not as firm as we are today. He was angel-like and walked over the newly created earth, veiled in a cloud. When evening came and Adam slept, his guardian angel brought his soul into heaven. Thus man knew no evil, was never ill and did not grow old. He did not know death.

When Adam walked over the earth, his soul was filled with joy. Full of trust, the animals came to him and greeted him. He gave them all names. The eagle came with all the other birds. The lion came with the panther. The zebra, giraffe, rhinoceros, and camel came, as did the bull, the horse and the stag. Further behind came the little animals, such as the beetles and ants and, of course, last of all, the snail. It had hurried along but was nonetheless last.

And God Father gave a garden to man. This was the Garden of Eden, or Paradise. Angels built a fence of light around the garden that Lucifer and his evil followers might not disturb the peaceful life within.

The Seventh Day

When everything had been created, God Father looked upon His work and saw that it was good. He gave the angels dominion over the new creation. The Elohim ruled over the sun and the sunlight, the moon and stars. The Cherubim held power over lightning and thunder. The rocks, the water, the air and the fire – all were given their rulers. Plants and animals, too, were given their heavenly masters.

It was a divine order that God Father made for the middle world. But, time and again, spirits rise up from the lower world and strive to pull down God's Kingdom or harm it in some way. That is the evil on earth. In order that man should be protected from evil, God Father gave him Paradise. Man was not to know of the evil in the world. Adam was to live an eternal life without knowing sorrow, illness or pain. Tirelessly, the angels descended to earth and rose heavenward again, bringing man divine light.

In Paradise

Once, as he was standing by the water watching the fish, Adam beheld his reflection. He thought, "O, had I a friend, that I might not be so alone."

During the night, when his angel brought his soul into heaven, God Father read Adam's wish. Then God created a companion for Adam. Hand in hand, like brother and sister, they wandered through the Garden of Eden. Adam showed her all the wonders of the creation. When she saw the beauty of all things, she cried out, "E!" and "Ah!" Therefore Adam called her, "Eva."

God Father showed them a tree in the midst of the garden and said, "You may eat the fruit of all the trees in the garden save this one alone. It is the Tree of Knowledge. Its fruit you may not eat."

At this time, human beings ate only fruit. There was no winter; it was always warm. Trees bore blossoms and fruit at the same time. All the animals were trusting and tame. Adam and Eve stroked them, and the animals came to eat from their hands. The birds ate the seeds that were strewn for them and circled about their heads. Such joy and peace reigned in the garden that Adam and Eve never even looked at the forbidden tree.

The angels had made a fence of light-rays around the garden, so that Lucifer might not enter. Every day they looked to make sure that there were no gaps. Once as Adam and Eve wandered through the garden, they came near the fence and heard a strange noise. At that very moment an evil spirit was struggling to get through the fence of light, but it did not succeed. The evil spirit saw the two human beings and reported to Lucifer what he had seen. From that time on, Lucifer pondered how he might get into the Garden of Eden.

Each time Adam and Eve ate the fruit of the Tree of Life, they were refreshed and heard the music of the heavens. Occasionally they sat upon the back of a horse or a deer and rode to the Four Rivers. There they dipped their feet into the water, whilst fish caressed them or leaped in silvery arches through the air. Butterflies lit upon their hands and shoulders or even upon their heads. It was as though they wore wreathes of flowers in their hair.

The Fall

Just as in our day the snake lives in hedgerows and fences, it liked to creep along the fence around Paradise. It happened that Lucifer saw the snake lying by the fence. He approached it stealthily and whispered, "Snake! Snake! Come to me! I have something to tell you! Look at the beautiful wings of the birds. What do you have? God is not just! See, the deer have long legs, but you must crawl upon the ground. Come to me; I will help to better your lot."

At first the snake hesitated, but then it crept out through a narrow crack. Lucifer said, "Open your mouth, and I will slip into your body. Then I can transform you." Lucifer slipped into the snake, and at once the snake began to glisten in many colors!

Lucifer whispered, "Creep into Paradise. There I can transform you even better." He steered the snake to the center of the garden toward the forbidden Tree of Knowledge and whispered, "Crawl into the tree!" So the snake wound itself around the trunk and into the branches.

Not long after, Adam and Eve walked by. They sat down by the Tree of Knowledge and listened to the angels' music, which resounded from heaven. All at once a strange voice called, "Eve, Eve!" Astounded, and a bit frightened, Eve went to see who had called her name. The voice continued, "Eve! This beautiful apple! Take it. An apple from this tree is better than that of any other. If you eat of this fruit, you shall know what Good and Evil are. You shall be like God." Eve was fearful and wanted to withdraw, but the snake talked and talked, and persuaded and coaxed, "Take, take it! No one will see."

Eve thought, "I could try just a little bite." She reached for an apple and bit into it. Then she gave it to Adam. O, woe! The cloud which had surrounded them fell away. Their step became so heavy that they could hardly lift their feet. The birds rose anxiously into the air. A strong wind began to blow and animals ran about in confusion. Quaking with fear, Adam and Eve hid behind the trees.

Thunder rumbled, and the Cherubim's lightning flashed across the sky. Then God Father's voice resounded, "Adam, where are you?"

"Here I am, behind the tree."

"Why are you hiding?"

"I am ashamed, O Father God, for I am naked."

Then Adam and Eve had to come forth, and God Father spoke in a mighty voice, "Since you have eaten of the Tree of Knowledge, you must leave this heavenly garden. You must go to earth. There you will toil and labor by the sweat of your brow. You will know sickness and death."

After God Father had spoken these words, a mighty fire-angel appeared. With a flaming sword, he drove Adam and Eve out of Paradise. The animals mourned plaintively and followed them with heavy tread. The wind wailed woefully through the trees. Flowers hung their blossoms and angels wept.

Archangel Michael and his loyal followers asked God Father, "May we still be guardian angels on the earth?" God Father granted this wish, else man would have been lost forever. The Cherubim, however, locked the gate of Paradise with their fiery swords and stood before it as its guardians.

On Earth

Michael accompanied Adam and Eve to the earth. In the evening, it grew cold. Shaking with cold, Adam and Eve built a small hut out of bushes and made garments of leaves. They gathered berries for food. As Eve was picking strawberries, she suddenly gave a piercing cry. A snake had frightened her! Wolves howled during the night. Hooting-owls with glowing eyes and leathery-winged, squeaking bats flew about. Adam and Eve were afraid to step outside their hut.

The next day, the second day on earth, Adam stepped upon a thorn, and mankind spilled the first drops of blood. He found tree-bark and tied it to his feet for protection. The ground in the hut was hard for sleeping, so Adam and Eve gathered moss from the stones and made the first bed. Adam found a tree full of beautiful ripe apples. He thought, "Perhaps Eve will be happy to have them!"

When he gave her the first apples on earth, Eve thought back to the lost Garden of Paradise and began to weep. Those were the first tears on earth. These apples did not taste as good as the fruit of Paradise. After eating them, Adam and Eve could no longer hear the heavenly music or the angels' voices.

One evening Michael came to Adam and Eve to comfort them. "You have not lost heaven completely. Pray to God. Then the thread of light, which binds your souls to heaven, will not tear. At night this thread draws you toward the heavenly light." From that time on, mankind has prayed to God. And the angel taught Adam to make a sacrifice. Through the fire and smoke Adam asked that the Light of God shine into human hearts.

The Sons of Cain

Cain and Abel

When Adam and Eve had lived on the earth for a time, Eve gave birth to a son. His name was Cain. Eve said to Adam, "Look upon this child. God has given him to me and put him in my care. I will be a good mother to him."

Adam took the boy up into his arms and said, "See, Eve! Heaven's fire shines from his eyes! His soul passed through the flaming gate of Paradise before he was born."

Cain had a strong, fiery soul. He grew to be tall and sturdy. Even the wild beasts fled before him. When lightning flashed and thunder rumbled, Cain shouted with joy. He sought to catch the lightning flashes! When he walked, the earth trembled beneath his feet.

After a time, Eve bore another son, who was named Abel. He was quite unlike Cain. Abel was gentle and delicate. Eve said to Adam, "See, Adam. All the radiance of heaven is in his eyes. His soul must have passed through the stars before it was born." Abel had a mild and gentle soul. His body grew to be slight and fragile. Abel befriended the sheep on the meadow. He played with them and became their shepherd.

Once Cain brought home a wooden stick, into which he had wedged a flat stone. "Father, I have found something!" he said. "I can turn the soil with it. I will call it a hoe." He dug holes in the ground and planted little trees in them. Cain loved to hoe the soil with his new tool. When he found a tree he liked, he tore it out by the roots and planted it in the field. With his hoe he made furrows in the soil and scattered seeds in them.

Abel loved flowers. He wound them into garlands and wore them upon his head. He moistened his fingers and held them out for the butterflies which sat trustingly upon them. The birds were his friends.

One time, the stone in Cain's hoe broke. He waded into the stream-bed to find another. He cracked the stones together until they split apart. Choosing the sharpest piece, he wedged it into the handle of the hoe. Abel saw this and said, "Dear brother Cain, you are covered with dust and soil." Thereupon, Cain threw himself into the racing stream and swam to the other shore! Cain never learned to swim; he could do it from the start.

Cain helped Abel build a fold for the sheep. He rammed posts into the earth while Abel wove supple willow branches between them. At night Abel brought the sheep into this fold so that they might be safe from the wild animals.

What Cain and Abel Dreamed

When Cain and Abel awakened from sleep in the mornings, they told each other their dreams. Cain said, "I went through rocks and crevices, deeper and deeper into the earth, until I came to the earth-fire. At this fire I lit a torch and carried it up to the earth's surface. With this fire, I brightened the darkness of night."

Abel said, "I walked with the angels in Paradise and looked for golden fruit but could not find any. In the middle of the garden I saw a cloud. It rose high up over the garden and shone as the morning sunlight. Behind the cloud was the tree that bears the golden fruit!"

Cain Conquers the Wolf

One morning, Abel went to his sheep. He saw blood upon the ground near the fold and tufts of wool scattered on the ground. There was a large hole where willow branches had been torn from the fence. During the night a wolf had come and killed a sheep. Weeping bitterly, Abel showed Cain what had happened. Cain's eyes flamed with anger. He uttered threatening words against the wolf. "Just wait, you wretched beast. I will not rest until I have found and punished you."

Abel crept into the fold where the trembling sheep huddled in a corner. He stroked them and comforted them. Cain tore up a stake and ran toward the forest. He crept into the undergrowth and listened intently. Suddenly he heard a noise. It came from behind some high rocks. With intent gaze, he crept nearer. Cautiously raising his head over the edge of the rocks, he saw a cave. Before it, a mother bear was playing with her cubs. "You are too brown," he muttered and crept on. A woodpecker hammered on a tree trunk. "He strikes that wood very well," Cain brought forth between clenched teeth. "But I will strike even harder."

Night began to fall. Cain had not found the wolf. He sat down to rest under a tree, but weariness overcame him, and soon he fell asleep. After a time, a shadow flitted by. It was the wolf. The beast lifted its muzzle, sniffed the air and stalked furtively toward Cain.

Unwittingly the wolf struck some leaves with his tail. Cain awakened to glowering eyes. Leaping up, he hurled his stake but missed. The wolf escaped. Thwarted and angered, Cain returned home.

He decided to spend the night in the sheep-fold, for the fence had not been mended. He said to Abel, "If the wolf comes, I will strangle him!" The sheep milled around restlessly and did not lie down until well past midnight. The moon rose, but Cain did not sleep. An owl hooted in the forest, but Cain did not sleep. He peered through the willow branches into the night that no shadow might escape him. What was that? Something was creeping stealthily along the edge of the forest. From time to time it stopped, crouched, and came nearer. Cain did not sleep. The wolf came near the fold. Finally he stuck his greedy head through the fence. Cain grasped and held him. The sheep bleated frantically, but Cain held fast and strangled the wolf to death.

When Abel awakened in the morning, he hurried to the fold. Cain was not there, and happily no sheep were missing. Then he saw Cain coming from the forest. From the distance he called to Abel, "I threw the wolf into the crevice in the forest. Your sheep are safe."

Abel mended the fence. That day he almost feared his brother, who had killed a wolf with his bare hands and had thrown him into a crevice.

When Eve Wept

One evening Adam and Eve sat by their hut, waiting for their sons. Cain came walking across a field, carrying golden-yellow apples he had picked. He placed them in Eve's lap. Eve took up one of the apples. As she looked at it, tears welled up in her eyes and rolled down her cheeks.

Startled, Cain asked, "Mother, why do you weep?" She gave no answer.

Then Abel came and asked sadly, "Mother, tell us, why do these beautiful apples make you weep?"

Speaking softly, Eve began, "Such apples as these, only much more beautiful, grew upon the trees in Paradise. Your father and I lived there like the angels. We were allowed to eat of all the fruits of the garden. Only the tree that stood mid-most in the garden was forbidden to us. Lucifer, the evil spirit, persuaded us to pick and eat an apple from that tree. He said, 'You will be like God.' We let ourselves be misled by him, and by that deed, we lost Paradise and its heavenly fruits!"

Cain asked, "Where is Paradise? I will find it and break open its gates!"

Eve answered, "No man will find it unless God Himself calls him."

Abel asked, "How can we please God?"

Eve replied, "By praying to him and bringing sacrifices. The fire and smoke may carry your prayers upward to God Father. That is what the angel of God taught us."

Cain exclaimed, "When I was splitting rocks, I saw sparks fly. I will try to kindle a fire. I will help you build a fire of sacrifice!" Thus Cain ignited the first fire. Abel brought kindling to feed the flames. Cain, however, threw such mighty limbs onto the fire that it flared up and set a nearby forest aflame. Then Adam taught him to build an altar of stones upon which the fire could burn more moderately.

How Cain Slew Abel

One day Abel said to Cain, "Let us bring an offering upon the altar as our father Adam has taught us."

Cain answered, "You make your offering, I will make mine." Cain built an altar of huge boulders and heaped much wood upon it. Abel's altar was small, with but little wood, for he was not as strong as Cain.

"What shall I bring as a sacrifice?" Abel asked his father.

"Give what you love most," answered Adam.

This answer filled Abel with dread. What he loved above all was a spotless, white lamb! Deep within himself he heard a voice saying, "Do not give that one. Take a spotted sheep. Any sheep is good enough for God." Again Abel was stricken with fear. Was this not an evil voice speaking to him? He went to the fold, caught his favorite lamb and sacrificed it. Cain brought fruits of the field to lay upon his altar and kindled the flame. Abel took some embers from Cain's altar to kindle his fire. In reverence Abel knelt down and prayed from the depth of his soul,

> I thank you, Father in the heavens,
> Who has created the beautiful world.
> I thank you for the sun
> Which lets plants and flowers grow,
> And warms animals and man.
> I thank you for the water, the air, and the earth
> Which nourish our bodies.
> Thank you for the living spirit
> Which you have breathed into me.

The smoke from Abel's sacrifice rose heavenward like a flower, but Cain's fire burned wildly. The flames spread in confusion. The smoke billowed near the ground and stung his eyes. He looked at

Abel's sacrifice and saw the smoke rising upward. Cain thought God had refused his sacrifice. He felt as if the wild fire was burning his soul. A powerful heat rose up into his head. Blinded with fury, he struck his brother a great blow. Abel fell to the ground, his last words a prayer. He was dead.

Cain lowered his hand. With horror he beheld the red blood, which was streaming from Abel's head and seeping into the soil. He knelt down and sobbed, "Abel, stand up! Abel, dear brother, wake up!" But Abel did not move. His starry eyes remained forever closed.

Then Cain felt a searing pain so deep that he cried out like a wild beast. Fear seized him and drove him through the forest. He ran wildly through thorns, bushes, rocks and ravines. A storm tore through the forests, and lightning flashed. Deep in a cave, he threw himself upon the ground. With his fists he beat the rocky floor and cried out, "Earth, break open and swallow me!" But the earth did not open.

And now, the voice of God sounded in his ears, "Cain, where is your brother, Abel?"

"I do not know. Am I my brother's keeper?" he groaned.

"What have you done? Your brother's blood is upon you. Restless and homeless you shall be. You shall roam the wide earth and never find peace."

Tears sprang into Cain's eyes and he said, "O Lord, my sin is too great to be forgiven. Where shall I flee before your countenance? Kill me!"

Then the voice of God spoke, "No one may kill Cain. This sign will protect you!" And he made a sign upon Cain's forehead. From that day on, Cain roamed the earth. Nowhere did he find rest.

Adam Buries Abel in the First Grave on Earth

In the evening after Cain and Abel had made their offerings, neither of them returned home to Adam and Eve. Adam went out to meet his sons. A faint trace of smoke led him to the place of sacrifice. Was that not Abel sleeping in the grass? He bent down to him and saw the blood on the ground. What was this? Indeed, Abel's body lay lifeless beside the altar! Deeply moved, Adam stood by the body of Abel, the first to die in the world. It seemed to Adam that he could hear voices from the clouds. They were the voices of the Cherubim that had driven him out of Paradise with the words, "On earth you shall suffer death."

Three days and three nights Adam watched over the body of Abel. He placed an offering upon the altar. When he brought Eve to the body of Abel, she wept and cried out, again and again, "Abel, dear Abel, stand up! Do you not hear me? Can you no longer be the light of my heart?" But Abel could not answer. She bedecked his body with flowers and kept watch together with Adam.

On the third day, Adam saw some ravens burying one of their kind in the earth. Then he recalled the words of the angel, "For you are earth and shall again become earth."

Then Adam dug a grave by the altar with Cain's hoe and, together with Eve, placed Abel's body into it. He said, "His body belongs to the earth, but his soul has returned to God."

After they had buried him, they felt comforted, and Eve said, "We will see Abel again in heaven, above the stars, when our time on earth is ended." Abel's grave was the first grave on earth.

Seth, the New Brother of Cain

In the evening, as Adam and Eve sorrowed over Abel, an angel appeared and said, "You shall have another son in place of Abel. He shall be as radiant as Abel and as strong as Cain. His name shall be Seth. Other sons and daughters will follow, so that there will be many people on earth. The soul of an angel will live in Seth, and he shall bring great light to mankind."

At the hour of Seth's birth, white doves flew in circles over Eve's hut. She heard the singing of the angels, who rejoiced that one of them had come to earth.

When Seth grew to boyhood, he did what Abel had done. He herded sheep, built altars, and brought offerings to God. As Seth was kneeling in prayer before his offering one day, Cain was roaming through the fields. He smelled the smoke and crept through the trees. When he saw the praying boy in the meadow, he thought that Abel had come back to life and walked toward him. Seth was startled by the powerful man he had never seen. Cain asked, "Who are you? Who are your parents?"

"I am Seth, the son of Adam."

When Cain understood that this was his brother, he embraced and kissed him, crying out, "O my brother, my brother!" Then, as suddenly as he had come, he let go of Seth and swiftly disappeared. Abel's blood left him no peace.

Time passed. Mother Eve bore many children, and the number of human beings on earth increased. They were still near to Paradise. They aged very slowly and lived for several hundred years.

An Angel Reveals the Book of Life to Adam

And it came to pass that an angel of God led Adam into a cave. The angel showed Adam a book in which seventy-two Signs of Light were written. All the wisdom of the world was written in the book. The angel taught Adam to read the signs in the book and said, "Before you die, you must give this book to a man whose soul is filled with the light of God, so that the wisdom of the angels may continue to shine on earth."

When Seth was twelve years old, and Adam saw that he was a divine child, he took him by the hand, and led him to the cave where the holy book was kept. The Book of Life was not written on parchment; it was Light written in Light. When Seth looked into it, he was blinded. He was unable to read the signs that were written in the script of the stars. Adam said, "When I die, you shall be the servant of the Book of Wisdom. Show it to no one, for it could be misused for harmful magic. When you have grown old, pass it on to someone from whose eyes the light of Paradise shines. If you find no such person, seal the entrance of the cave. Then the book will be safe for later times."

Adam's Death

Adam had grown very old. The earth drew him toward her with ever greater force until he was quite bent over when he walked. When he knew that he would die before long, he said to Seth, "My dear son! Soon my soul will go to God. My body, however, belongs to the earth. Will you, my son, fulfill a last request for me?"

"All that I am able to do," Seth answered.

"Go toward the rising sun. Let the angel of the Lord guide you to Paradise, and bring me three seeds from the Tree of Life. Place them in my coffin. From the seeds a tree will grow, which will bring blessing to mankind."

Seth asked, "Father Adam, will I find Paradise? Whom shall I call upon to be my guide?"

Adam answered, "Paradise has been lifted into heaven. You will never find it on earth. Call upon Michael, he will guide you."

Seth wandered toward the sunrise until he came near to the cave of the Holy Book. He went into the cave to rest and fell into a deep sleep. The Archangel Michael came to him and led his soul to heaven and into the Garden of Paradise. The flaming gate was guarded by the Cherubim, and lightning flashed from the gate. Michael took Seth's soul under his wing and carried it through the portal to the Tree of Life. Seth picked one apple, broke it open and took three seeds from it. Then Michael carried Seth back through the lightning and fire, back to the cave.

When Seth awakened, he found the seeds in his hand. He hurried back to Father Adam, around whom people had gathered. The news that Adam lay dying had travelled far and wide. Sons, daughters, grandchildren – all had come to be near Adam in this hour. When Seth came to him with the three seeds, he placed them into Adam's mouth. One last time Adam raised himself. Then he stretched out his arms toward the angel of death, who was sent to guide his soul.

Gently the angel lifted the soul from the body of man's ancestor. Then Adam's heart stood still, his breathing slowed and his limbs grew rigid.

Lucifer had been waiting for this moment. He thought, "Adam belongs to me. His soul belongs in my kingdom!" He came near to the angel of death in order to snatch Adam's soul. But Michael was there. Against him, the fiend of darkness had no power and was forced to flee.

Seth took Adam's casket into the cave where the Holy Book was kept. He had read in the book that in a time to come the casket would be carried far away, into the region where the Messiah, the Redeemer of mankind, would be born. He had read that a tree would grow from the three seeds. The wood of that tree would yield three things: the staff of a Divine Leader, the pillars of a Temple and the cross of the Redeemer.

From then on, Seth lived near the cave and came to be known among men as a priest of the Lord. All those who witnessed the offerings Seth made to God felt heavenly light pour into their souls.

The Sons of Cain

In those times, the earth was a vast wilderness and wild animals lived everywhere. Herds of wild horses and cattle grazed on the plains and belonged to no one. Bushes and trees served as protection to human beings. No one knew how to build houses! People ate the fruits of the trees and the fields, such as Cain had offered in his sacrifice to God. No hunter hunted animals, for no one ate meat. Then three sons were born to Cain. Their names were Jabal, Jubal and Thubal-Cain. Through them, much was changed on the earth, for the sons and daughters of Cain loved to work.

Jabal, the Tamer of the Animals

When Jabal was a young man, he had a strange dream. He dreamed of wild horses racing over the plains. His heart leapt when he beheld their magnificent jumps and playful games. At that time, no one had thought of riding horses. Thus Jabal was very surprised when, in his dream, a being approached him and told him to mount a horse! At that moment, a splendid white horse trotted by. As it raced by, Jabal leapt upon its back. Swift as the wind the white steed carried him over the field. They came to a river and the horse prepared to leap to the other side. Jabal struggled to hold fast, but, losing his grip, he fell into the chilly water!

Full of amazement, Jabal woke up to find that he had been sleeping under a tree! Not far away, a herd of wild horses was grazing. At once he thought, "I will capture a horse and ride it, just as I did in my dream. I will creep up to the herd and try to leap on the back of one of them. But I must be clever, for they are wary and quick."

Taking cover behind a clump of bushes, Jabal waited tensely until a horse came near his hiding place. A black stallion with a gleaming coat approached. A leap and a bound, and Jabal thought he was on the horse's back! But the horse reared high, turned and threw him to the ground before he could even grasp its mane. Ashamed of his failure, Jabal got to his feet – while the herd of horses neighed shrilly and ran off. Fiery determination consumed Jabal. "I must succeed," he told himself. From then on, the thought of catching and riding a horse never left him. For days on end he roamed the fields and plains. Again and again, he tried to approach the herd, but the horses always caught his scent in their delicate nostrils and fled.

One day, after fruitless effort, Jabal was very thirsty. He could not find a spring or brook anywhere. He saw a herd of grazing cows and a calf nursing at the cow's udder. Jabal was tremendously strong. He caught the cow by the horns, bent her head to the side and threw her to the ground. He squeezed milk from her udder and drank it greedily. It was sweet and refreshing. No human being had ever drunk milk before! From then on, Jabal often caught cows and drank their milk.

After a time, Jabal discovered a pasture with shady trees under which the wild horses sought rest. Early one morning, when the horses had gone to drink, he climbed one of the trees and hid in the leaves. The wild horses returned and, sensing no danger, stood in the shade of the trees. All at once, there was a rustling in the leaves, and with a rush, Jabal jumped on the back of a white horse standing directly below him. He lay firmly upon its back and clasped his arms around the horse's neck. The horse snorted angrily, and in a frenzy, ran into the field. It reared upon its hind legs, but Jabal held fast. Then it galloped wildly with him over sticks and stones, over ditches, and brooks. When Jabal did not fall off, it threw itself upon the ground and rolled on its back. But Jabal quickly knelt upon the horse's neck and pressed its head to the ground so that the hooves kicked empty air.

Finally the horse grew tired and knew that it had been conquered. When it lay spent and still, Jabal stroked its neck and spoke soothing words to it. He patted its back and scratched its ears. A few days later, the horse was tame. Man and horse were friends. High on his horse, he rode over the earth.

People, however, were afraid of the horse and its rider. They thought it a monster and ran away in fear. Children cried out to their parents, "A monster, a monster! It has six legs and two heads, and it looks as though a man is growing on top of it!" When the people fled in fear, Jabal laughed and dismounted. He bound the horse to a tree with a rope made of reeds and persuaded the people to come out from their hiding places. They came forth warily but kept their distance. A brave boy, whom Jabal took up in his arms, even stroked the horse's neck. Then the adults also gathered round. Suddenly the horse neighed. Everyone screamed and ran. Jabal laughed and explained that horses make such sounds when they are happy.

Nearby there were several huts. Jabal saw that the children were all very pale and thin. A woman wailed, "This year we found only very little fruit. We have been digging for roots and eating them."

Jabal said, "I will tame a cow for you, and then you shall have milk."

"Now, what do you suppose that means?" they said to each other and shook their heads in disbelief.

Jabal tied his horse to a tree and said to a man standing there, "Guard my horse for me. I will come back in the evening." On foot he went into the nearby hills where he has seen a herd of cattle grazing. From a hiding place he ran toward the herd and grasped a cow by the horns. At that moment, a large bull bellowed and charged toward Jabal. He let go of the cow and seized the bull. A tremendous wrestling followed. Finally, Jabal pressed the bull's head to the ground with such force that the bull was conquered and knew who was master. Defeated, the beast stomped off.

Now Jabal had to stalk the herd once more to capture a cow. It was easier to subdue a cow than a bull! He brought the captured animal back to the people. The children cried, "He's coming with a horned monster!" and ran into hiding.

But brave little Lemo, who had patted the horse, dared to come near. Jabal tied the cow near the horse, stroked her and milked her. "White blood! White blood!" cried Lemo, when he saw the milk squirting from the cow's udder.

Jabal laughed and said to him, "That is milk. It is good to drink." He squirted milk into his hand and drank it and then let Lemo taste it. It tasted so good that he asked for more. He called to the others, "White blood, good milk!" Cautiously they came near. Jabal gave one of them some milk, then a second, and a third. He asked for a bowl and filled it with milk.

While they were all crowded around the milk, the cow suddenly bellowed, "Moo!" Again everyone screamed and scattered. Only Jabal, Lemo and the man with the bowl did not run. They laughed heartily.

Jabal said to the man with the bowl, "You may keep the cow. She will give you good milk every day. Give the milk to the children and take good care ot her. I will come back again and catch more cows for you. You are a strong man. Why not go to a herd and capture one?" Then Jabal mounted his horse and rode on. He thought, "Maybe I can tame other animals besides horses and cows." He felt a great desire to do so.

* * *

Jabal once came to a mountain range. The people living there told him, "Horned demons live in the mountains. They climb high onto the rocks. No one dares to go there."

Jabal replied, "I dare. I will see what kind of animals they are." He asked a man to take care of his horse and climbed up the rocky mountains. Suddenly he came upon mountain goats grazing and resting on the patches of grass. They showed no fear. When evening came, the whole herd of them began climbing in one direction. Jabal followed them to an enormous cave, in which they lay down. He too went into the cave and stayed there through the night.

In the morning, Jabal noticed that many of them went to a rock and licked it. He found salt in the rock and put a chunk of it into his leather bag. The goats let Jabal milk them. Their milk tasted sweet. Some of the animals grew so fond of Jabal that they followed him wherever he went. He led them into the valley, giving them salt from time to time. That is how goats came to be with human beings. Jabal gave the goats to the mountain-dwellers and taught them to build folds and fences. By and by the mountain people themselves caught mountain goats and tamed them, for they prized their sweet milk.

As Jabal was making his way through a dense forest one day, he heard horrible screaming and spitting sounds. He found a large wildcat fighting with a small one. He chased the large one off and took the little one up in his arms. He stroked its ruffled fur and put the little creature into his pocket. When he came to the people to whom he had given the cow, he gave the small cat some milk. The cat became fast friends with Jabal, purred and rubbed her back against his legs. Wherever Jabal went, the cat went also. When he and his horse rested, the cat stalked mice. It happened, however, that once after he had visited some people living in bush houses, the cat did not come at his call. He looked for her and found her underneath a bush with seven little kittens! Since then, there have been house-cats.

Another time, Jabal heard the howling and whining of young wild dogs. Their mother had probably left them, since they were no longer small. Jabal took one of them along and taught him to sit behind him upon the horse's back. Whenever the dog fell off, he would run joyfully at the horse's side. Jabal taught him to fetch sticks and other tricks. At night, the dog slept near his master and the horse.

One day, Jabal fell asleep in the shade of a tree, his horse grazing nearby. The dog lay at Jabal's feet. A thief, intent on stealing the horse, was slowly creeping toward it. Suddenly the dog jumped up, barked fiercely, and chased after the man. When he caught the fellow, he bit him in the leg. Jabal awoke and realized what a watchful creature he had.

From that day on, Jabal tamed dogs for people. Besides being watchdogs, they were also helpful to shepherds and goatherds.

Jubal Brings Music to Humankind

Another of Cain's sons was Jubal. In the daytime, when the sun shone, Jubal was sad. At night, when the stars sparkled, Jubal was happy. Why was that? When night came and Jubal went to sleep, he had the most wonderful dreams. In his dreams he walked through the rainbow-colored portal of heaven, where angels sang and played music. The stars resounded like the ringing of bells. When he heard the angels sing, he would softly join in their song. But, whenever Jubal awakened, he would forget all the songs!

At that time, human beings had no instruments, nor could they sing. This is why Jubal was sad. Often he thought, "If only I could sleep, dream, and sing in the heavenly house forever. I wish I never had to return to earth." When he lay down to sleep the next evening, he prayed to his guardian angel, "Take me away from this sad earth, where no songs or music gladdens my heart."

Then his guardian angel appeared and said, "Jubal, God has heard your plea. He has pity on you and mankind. You, Jubal, shall be a great singer. You may bring to mankind songs and music such as you hear in heaven. You shall bring them as a consolation for the heaven that was lost." With these words, he gave Jubal a golden cup and made him drink of it. No sooner did Jubal drink of the cup than he heard the music of heaven and stars ring mightily in his ears.

When he awoke, the music rang on! It resounded through him so that the songs poured from his lips. He went among the people and sang his songs. To the shepherds he sang the shepherd's song, to the farmers, the song of the fields. The sun, the stars and the moon that rises at evening – all were praised with music and hymns. His songs brought comfort to all who were sad. He sang to the children of how God had created the world, how the robin warbles and the horse trots. People did not forget the songs. They sang them and passed them on from generation to generation.

Thubal-Cain, the Inventor and Smith

The third of Cain's sons was called Thubal-Cain. He loved the soil, the sturdy trees, and the caves in the rocks. He said, "I will find the hardest rocks of the earth and shape tools from them."

He found iron. It was so hard that it could not be broken into pieces. He dreamed of softening it with fire. But when he placed it in a mighty fire, the iron did not become soft. With stones and clay he built an oven, which he fired to such heat that the iron became malleable. He drove a hole through a flattened piece of metal and fastened a wooden handle to it. In this way he made a hoe which was much sturdier than the old stone and wooden hoes that had been in use until then. These hoes he made for the farmers. Using his clenched fist as a model, he wrought the first hammer of iron. The iron hammer was so hard that with it, Thubal-Cain could crack any stone. He made the first iron anvil and placed it in a cave, which became his smithy.

The Sons of Cain and the First Houses

It happened that Jabal slept on a hilltop. He dreamed of a heavenly city, with temples, towers, and houses, through which men went in and out. Full of rapture, he looked upon the strange buildings and thought, "If only I could build such houses on earth." When he awakened, he began to build houses of stones, wood, and clay. They were as small as toys. He labored tirelessly for many days.

Thubal came by and said after studying the little toy-city, "You should build these houses strong and large enough for men to live in. I will forge tools so that you may fell trees! Instead of splinters of wood, you must use tree-trunks. I will make a plan."

Jubal also came to the hill and found pleasure in the little houses. He said, "You will need strong men to help you. I will sing them a song of housebuilding. Then they will follow me and help you."

* * *

After some days had passed, Jabal mounted his white steed and rode deep in the woods to the cave where his brother Thubal-Cain worked. Smoke billowed from the entrance, and such clanging and banging resounded that the horse shied and refused to go near the cave. Tying his horse to a tree, Jabal walked toward the cave. How startled he was when two sooty fellows came out! "Is Thubal there?" he asked. They grinned and pointed to the cave. Jabal heard the crackling fire and the deafening clang of iron hammers. Through the smoke, he saw the large, ghostly form of his brother wielding a hammer with tremendous blows.

Finally, Thubal stopped and wiped the sweat from his brow. Seeing Jabal, he laughed, "You don't like my fiery hell?"

Jabal answered, "Have you made tools with which I can build houses?"

Thubal took up a tong and grasped a glowing piece of iron. "Here, it is – nearly finished." He struck the forward edge of the iron a few quick blows, then went outside and thrust it into a nearby brook to cool it. Then he went to a tree and cut off a thick branch. Finally, he forced the branch through a hole in the dull end of the metal. This was the first axe. With powerful blows, Thubal now struck the axe against the trunk of the tree from which he had cut the branch. Chips flew and, after a short time, the huge tree crashed to earth. Jabal felt a kind of awe toward the little iron wedge in Thubal's hand as he looked at the enormous tree that was felled.

Then Thubal brought something else from the cave. He showed Jabal a strange, jagged, long piece of iron and said, "With the teeth in my mouth I can crush bits of wood. I have made iron teeth which bite wood!" They went to a fir tree and began to saw. They sweated and struggled but finally succeeded in cutting through the trunk.

The saw often stuck fast because its teeth were thick and irregular. jabal said, "I like the axe better."

Thubal answered, "I'll forge new and better saws." Then Thubal's companions began forging axes for Jabal.

On that day, Jubal came with ten stout men who wanted to help Jabal build houses. Soon the sound of chopping and crashing trees rang through the forest. By the third day, trees enough for the first house had been felled. The slender stems were hewn to points and cut into pieces twice the height of a man. Two men would lie on the trunk as the measure so that the stems could be cut to the right lengths. The first house Jabal built was round. The trunks were rammed into the ground in a circle. Cattails and reeds growing in a nearby lake were used to cover the roof. But before the roof was completed, Seth was called that he might bless the house.

Seth said to the assembled people, "This house shall be a small Paradise, a small Eden, into which evil shall not enter. Make an

offering place in the middle of the house that we may consecrate it. Put a small tree on the house's gable in memory of the tree of Paradise."

When all was ready, a great crowd of people assembled. Jabal, Jubal, and Thubal helped Seth light the sacrificial fire. As the smoke rose upward, Jubal joyfully sang a song of consecration:

The house on earth is raised.
May no fire destroy it,
May lightning not strike it,
A good spirit dwell in it,
Banish all danger
And protect it from floods.
Peace be with this place,
Blest be this house,
All who live therein,
And all who come and go.

As Jubal sang, the smoke rose heavenward. When the offering fire burned low and the last embers glowed in the pit, Jabal and the other builders covered the roof with reeds. No one, however, knew to whom the house belonged. When it was completed, Jabal said, "The first house on earth shall be dedicated to God. I give it to His priest, Seth."

From then on, Seth lived in the house and kept it as a holy place. Men called it the House of God. After that, Jabal and his builders built houses everywhere, but none was ever roofed until after an offering had been made.

The Three Knives

Seth said to Thubal-Cain, “Can you forge a token of pure gold that resembles a ray of the sun? When we make sacrifices, I will thrust it into the earth, that the fields, too, may be blessed. Give it a handle of iron that I may grasp it.” He gave Thubal a piece of gold that he had found in the mountains. With great art and skill, Thubal and his smiths forged a golden knife. From then on, when making an offering, Seth prayed for God’s blessing and for the sun to warm the seeds and the soil. As a sign of this, he would thrust the golden knife into the earth. Only after this had been done, the plow and the hoe were allowed to turn the soil.

* * *

Jubal once slept under a large bush. In his dream, an angel appeared and played music upon a heavenly instrument. It looked like a tube with several small holes in it. Jubal asked the angel, “May I also play such an instrument? I should so like to.”

The angel pointed toward the bush. “Take wood from these branches and make the instrument.”

Jubal awoke. He broke a branch from the bush, went to Thubal-Cain and told him of his dream. Thubal said, “I will forge a silver knife. With it, we can carve the instrument from the wood.” Skillfully Thubal forged a knife of silver and with it carved the first flute out of wood. It was a perfect copy of the heavenly flute.

* * *

One of Thubal-Cain’s helpers secretly forged a knife of iron. He thought, “This is a tool that will surely have many uses.” When it was finished, he hid it in a crack in the cave.

Jubal Makes Music for the Animals

Jubal had seen another strange instrument in a dream. When he told Thubal-Cain of it, Thubal formed a lyre from wood. The strings were made from sheep gut, which was twisted, stretched, and dried in the air.

Jubal sat in the forest under a tree and played his lyre. Curious mice slipped out of their hiding places, listened to the music and began to dance. After a time, they kept still and listened. A wildcat came and detected the mice. But Jubal's music sounded so sweet that she forgot the mice and lay down at his feet. Not a mouse ran away. Two rabbits heard the music. They hobbled to the cat, sat down beside her, and wiggled their ears to the music.

A fox crept up to the clearing. When he saw the many small creatures, his mouth drooled. "I'll rush in and have three meals in one!" But the strains of Jubal's lyre stilled his hunger, and his bushy tail began to wag to the rhythm of the music. He lay down beside the rabbits.

The bushes rustled, and a wolf appeared! With his sharp eye he had seen the animals and was contemplating, "Shall I take the fox, the cat or the rabbit?" But Jubal's music reached his ears, and though he pawed them as if to ward off flies, he too was forced to lie down. With his head on his paws and his eyes closed, he listened to the music.

Branches cracked in the undergrowth. An enormous bear came lumbering out of the woods. When he heard Jubal's music, he rose up on his hind legs and danced into the clearing. He danced and lolled about, until he tumbled down and lay comfortably on his belly.

All the animals lay around Jubal while he played. Gradually they all fell asleep. Jubal smiled and thought to himself, "In Paradise the animals were as peaceful as this." When darkness began to fall, he rose and left the forest.

All was dark when the mice awakened. Seeing the wildcat, they scampered into their holes. Then the rabbits awakened. Frightened, they looked around and dashed into the underbrush. The wildcat yawned and stretched, saw the fox and wolf, and melted into the shadows. The fox yawned and opened his eyes. Catching scent of the wolf and bear he asked, "What am I doing here?" Quickly he sneaked away.

The wolf scratched his nose. "What? I've been sleeping near a bear!" Swiftly he ran off.

The bear awoke only the next morning. Astonished, he looked around. "What a dream I had – mice, rabbits, fox, wildcat, wolf – and a man playing music! That was a marvellous dream. I'd like to dream it again." And contentedly he ambled toward his cave.

Jubal Plays for Men

Naamah, one of Cain's daughters, had woven a long white robe for Jubal. When he rode upon his white horse wearing the white robe, he looked like a messenger of God. At night he would rest at the edge of a forest or on the top of a hill. Often he played his flute under the gleaming stars. No wild animal ever did him harm. One night he rested upon a hill, not realizing that a village was nearby. His horse had lain down at his feet. As he began to play upon his flute, in one of the huts a young girl awakened. She nudged her brother and said, "Listen! A nightbird is singing."

"No," the boy whispered. "It is surely the voice of an angel. I have never heard a bird whistle like that. Come, we'll go outside and listen." The children's father and mother were sound asleep and did not hear the children go out. The music came from the hilltop, where they could see a white form.

Afraid to climb the hill alone, they awakened their parents. "Listen," they said. "Music is sounding from the hill." Full of amazement, the parents listened. Filled with awe and wonder, they took their children by the hand and slowly climbed the hill. Halfway up, they stopped and, in the moon- and star-light, they saw the white form more clearly. A melody so pure and gentle rang through the stillness that they fell on their knees and bowed their heads. After a while, more people awakened and gathered at the foot of the hill. They did not dare to climb up the hill for fear of disturbing the music.

Then Jubal took up his lyre and sang. The music resounded afar. He sang and played untilsunrise. Then he mounted his horse, and, lifting his hand in greeting, he rode down the hill. In awe the people bowed their heads before him. Soon he disappeared behind dark trees. The people of the village built a stone altar where he had sung, and they brought offerings to the heavenly powers who had spoken to them through Jubal's music.

Jubal often met children on his wanderings. He played for them and taught them to sing simple songs. Whenever he rode out, the children would follow after him until night fell. They would beg and plead for more songs. Even the smallest of them began to hum and sing. The older ones whittled whistles and pipes. Thus ever more singing and playing filled the lives of the earth's people.

Of Wicked Companions and Their Evil Deeds

Thubal-Cain and his companions left his cave one day in order to dig for iron. Two workers remained behind to tend the fire and finish forging a hoe. The older man, Kenos, was holding the red-hot iron with a tong, while the other struck it so that the sparks flew. One stroke glanced off the anvil and struck Kenos' side. Furious, Kenos dealt the careless fellow a blow with his fist. He, in turn, dropped his hammer and struck Kenos in the neck. A fierce wrestling began and shortly both men were rolling and grappling on the floor of the cave. Kenos felt himself weakening, when his eye lit upon the iron knife in the crack. He grasped it, attacked his enemy and stabbed him to death.

When he had done this deed, he was shocked and frightened. Seeing the blood streaming, he left the knife and ran away. Although fury still raged in his blood, he thought he heard the mocking laughter of demons behind him. He ran frantically through the forest. A gale howled through the tree tops, lightning flashed in the distance, and rain gushed through the fir and oak trees.

After stumbling through the forest, Kenos found a cave. Exhausted, he collapsed on the floor. Between clenched teeth he muttered, "He often aggravated me. Now he has his reward." With no remorse or regret in his heart, he pressed his head upon his arms and fell asleep.

Toward evening of the next day, Thubal and his companions returned. "What is this?" he asked, when he saw no smoke rising from the cave. The fire had gone out. When they entered, one of them stumbled over the body of the dead man. Shouts and sounds of dread echoed. In the darkness no one could see who was lying on the floor, so they carried the body outside. One man drew the knife from the dead man's chest and said dully, "Kenos has stabbed him to death!"

Thubal looked at the blood-stained knife for a long time and said at last, "I forged the golden knife for Seth, the priest, to bring divine offerings. Jubal, the singer, carries the silver one. The iron knife has brought misfortune. Shall I bury it deep in the earth? Throw it into a ravine?" But then he thought: "Cain killed Abel without a weapon. The knife is not guilty. Kenos is the murderer, and he has fled." He thrust the knife into the ground several times to wipe off the blood. Then he placed it back into the crack in the rocks.

Kenos in the Forest Cave

During the first night that Kenos slept in the forest cave, an evil spirit crept to his side and whispered, "Go. Fetch the knife from Thubal' s cave. With the knife you will have power over men! You can kill animals with it and eat their meat. You can still your hunger."

Early in the morning, Kenos crept back to Thubal's cave and hid behind the rocks and trees. He waited until he saw the master and his companions walking to the brook where they washed each morning. Then he crept into the empty cave and cautiously felt about in the darkness. He was not mistaken. The knife was in the crack! He felt as though the drops of blood on the floor of the cave whispered his name and reached out for him. Quickly he seized the knife and, in wild flight, dashed out of the cave into the forest.

Suddenly, a ferocious wild-eyed wolf stood before him! Kenos leaped upon him, stabbed him to death and drank his blood. Then he dragged the grim creature to his secret cave. As Thubal had taught him, he struck sparks from stones and lit a fire. Then he roasted the wolf's meat and stilled his hunger. The wolf-skin served him for a bed.

News of the murder Kenos had committed reached the ears of the priest, Seth. He called the people together to make an offering of atonement in his Holy House. When the fire had been lit and the prayers said, Jubal played his lyre. In a sacred dance the priests and priestesses moved around the altar. Meanwhile, Kenos had crept near to the huts! From the distance, he saw the sacrifice and the many people on their way to the Holy House. Not far from the village, he found a young man lazily lying on a bear skin. When Kenos asked him why he was not at the sacrifice, the fellow answered, "I am too lazy; I felled a tree yesterday."

Kenos was so pleased to find another who stayed away from the offering that he sat down beside the fellow and showed him his dagger. "Come with me, and I will teach you how to use a knife like this. Maybe I can get one for you!" After a bit of persuasion, the man followed Kenos into the woods. Together they killed a wild pig, roasted some of the meat at the fire in their cave, and had enough to eat for several days.

From then on, the two men hunted together. They frightened the animals and carried evil in their hearts. They did not spare doe or buck. They began to kill animals not only for their meat, but for the pleasure in the hunting and killing.

One time, Thubal sent away one of his helpers because he had cursed at his work and used the name of God in vain. Grimly the man strayed about the countryside. Kenos and his friend found him sleeping in the wet leaves. He suited them so they invited him to come with them to their cave. Now they were three.

How Jubal Escapes Great Danger

It happened that Jubal came to the forest where the wicked men dwelt. Night fell, and to his surprise, he saw fire-light shimmering between the trees. When he came closer, he saw three men squatting around a fire. "Hello!" he called to them. Startled, the three leaped to their feet and disappeared among the dark trees and bushes. Suspecting nothing, Jubal laughed at their fear. He sat down by the fire and called, "Come back, woodsmen! There is room for all of us by the fire." The men did not come back, however, because they feared Jubal would betray them. They decided to kill him. As they crept nearer, Jubal began to play upon his harp. The music was so lovely, in the stillness, that they forgot their evil plan. They came from their hiding places and lay down by the fire. The hearts of the two younger men were softened by the heavenly music. It was as though a light had been lit in their souls. Tears streamed from their eyes.

But the murderer Kenos gnashed his teeth. The evil spirit whispered into his ear, "See, he is enchanting your companions. Break his harp! Stop his singing!"

"May I spend the night here?" Jubal asked. Kenos nodded slyly and led Jubal to the back of the cave. He spread out a bearskin for him and soon they all lay down. Near to his sleeping place, Kenos stuck the dagger into the earth.

As Jubal was about to fall asleep, an angel appeared to him and said, "Play on your harp, Jubal. Do not stop until all the men are soundly sleeping, for one of them harbors evil towards you." Jubal took up his harp and played a lullaby. Only when he knew that the three men slept soundly did he, too, lay down to sleep.

Early the next morning the chirping, twittering birds awakened Jubal. He rose from his bed in a happy mood and, while the three men slept soundly, he went on his way. As he walked through the woods, he sang and played on his harp. The birds flew before him from tree to tree and guided him out of the forest.

The Death of Seth

As long as Seth lived among men, he strengthened them through his light and his words. He brought much wisdom to them from the Book of Adam. Seth was the ancestor of the priests, who brought offerings to God on behalf of the people. Men everywhere made holy offerings and served the Divine Beings. There were few evil people. These lived in the mountainous forests by hunting. Occasionally they stole what they needed from the huts of peaceful people.

As time went on, more and more houses were built in the lowlands. Tamed herds of cows, goats, and sheep became ever more numerous. While people worked, they offen sang songs they had learned from Jubal. They sang about the wondrous works of God. There were many smithies like Thubal's, where blacksmiths made tools for the farmers and builders. A few people had learned from Thubal the art of crafting musical instruments. They made harps, horns, and flutes.

When Seth was very old and knew that he would die before long, he looked for someone to whom he could entrust the Book of Adam. But he could find no one whose light of soul was so strong as to withstand the Light of the Book. So Seth hid the Book, sealed the entrance of the hidden cave, and not long after died. Men mourned his death deeply. In sadness the priests prepared the funeral sacrifice. They asked, "Who will tell us the Will of God, now that Seth has gone from us?"

How Enos Brought the Worship of Idols to Mankind

Enos had learned from Seth how God had created man from the earth and how man was given a soul through God's divine breath. But Enos had become a scoffer and had joined the band of evildoers. He said, "I, too, will create a being and give it living breath!" He formed a clay idol with a frightful face. Placing it upon an altar, he lit the fire and breathed upon it. His false offering attracted an evil being. This spirit slipped into the idol and gained power over Enos and his friends. They began to serve the evil spirit and practice black magic.

In this way, ever more wickedness came among men. They came from their hideaways in the mountains and carried out many misdeeds. With long knives, which they called swords, they frightened and killed people who opposed them. Evil increased. Many men practiced black magic to cause harm and chaos. Four things changed in this time of Enos: the mountains hardened completely, deserts appeared, men lost the image of God, and evil beings lost their fear of men. Those who worshipped idols painted jagged black lines on their foreheads, as a sign that they were true companions of Enos and servants of evil demons.

After a long time, only a few loyal people continued to bring offerings with the priests of the tribe of Seth. Jubal's songs were heard no more; flute and harp were silent. Sadness and sorrow reigned over the angels in heaven, and their cry over the corruption of man reached unto God.

Through Enoch the Light of Goodness Returns to Earth

God chose the great courageous soul of Enoch and directed Enoch's eyes earthward. Enoch saw the darkness surrounding man. Cursing, wailing, complaining, and the sounds of war resounded from earth. He said, "The bright image of man is surrounded by the dragon. Voices of misery and torment rise up from the depths. 0 Lord! Send me to earth to save men with light of Your own Light. I will dare to save men for your kingdom! I will fight against evil on earth." When Enoch had spoken these words, God Father gave him light of His own Light.

After a time, Enoch was born on earth as a little child. His soul shone so brightly that the house of his parents was filled with light. A maid hurried to the fields to bring his father the happy news of the birth of a son.

When the father came, he saw many white birds encircling his home. They circled higher and higher until they disappeared into the blue of the sky. At the threshhold of the house, a radiant light shone toward him. He found a small child lying at his mother's side. The child' s eyes shone like the sun. Tenderly the father took the child up into his arms.

At that hour, an old man came to the house. The old man had known Seth! A dream had foretold him the birth of Enoch, and he said to the parents of Enoch, "Rejoice with me! In your son, the light of Seth has come to earth again! Now I may die in peace, for I know a new messenger of God has been sent to men. As long as my feet will carry me, I will go forth and proclaim that Enoch is born, the greatest priest since Seth!"

Enoch Makes His First Offering

The evil spirits tried to come near Enoch when he was a child but in vain. His guardian angel protected him from all danger. When he was a young man, he went into the city where many idol-worshippers lived. He saw them dancing wildly round and round a large idol, and he heard their blasphemous words.

A holy wrath came over Enoch. His words thundered forth so loudly that the clay idol began to sway and totter. With a powerful thrust, he cast it to the stone floor, and it broke into pieces with a violent crash. The idol-worshippers cried out in anger; many of them ran away. Others stared at Enoch in horror. He called out: "Wipe the jagged black lines from your foreheads! Your demon has fled. The Light of God will live again among men. Bring wood! We will make a sacrifice and offer prayers!"

The people were so overwhelmed by Enoch that they could not do otherwise than heed him. They brought wood, and soon a fire of sacrifice was burning upon the stone pedestal on which the idol had stood. Enoch spoke holy words into the flames. The assembled people were impressed by Enoch's courage and wiped the signs from their foreheads. A great number gathered around the new offering. From that time on, Enoch wandered from place to place helping human souls find the realm of heaven.

Enoch Finds the Cave of the Holy Book

Enoch was resting by a brook one day, when a majestic angel appeared to him. At first he thought, "Has my time come to die?"

"No," said the angel. "I am sent by God to show you the cave in which Seth sealed the Book of Adam." The angel led him to the cave. Enoch broke through the wall and entered the holy chamber. It was a wide, light-filled cave, whose walls glistened and gleamed with crystals. He had to turn his face away from the brightness of the book. As he did so, he saw a casket. The angel said to him, "Here lies the body of Adam. It has been kept for future times and will one day be carried to another place."

Now the angel taught Enoch to read the book in which the wisdom of the world had been written. Enoch remained in the cave for a very long time. His body needed neither food nor drink, since he stood in the Light of God and was nourished by Him. Enoch returned to men, his soul filled with wisdom and holy light.

Enoch's Wanderings

Once as Enoch was wandering through a forest, he heard loud shouts and laughter. "Those are people," he thought, "who sound like ruffians. Shall I avoid them and go my way in another direction?" He stood still a moment and then said to himself, "The light shall shine in the darkness. I will go to them, whoever they may be." He went toward the clearing from which the raucous voices sounded and came upon a band of robbers. They sat around a fire, roasting meat. Enoch saw that they had all drawn the jagged black lines on their foreheads. He greeted them with a powerful voice.

So great was their surprise and respect that not one of them dared to oppose him. They ceased shouting and laughing, and they invited him to come to the fire. No one had ever seen Enoch before, and all wondered, "Who might this bold wanderer be who fearlessly sits down with robbers?" Without saying a word, the robbers chewed their meat and gnawed on the bones.

Enoch looked into the flames and said, "In the beginning, God created the heavens, the earth, and man out of light and fire. Everything came into being through Him. From Him, all life sprang. All that grows on the trees of the forest, that creeps on the ground or flies in the air and that shines upon man and warms him, all has its being in God."

Full of astonishment, the robbers listened to Enoch speak of the seven days of creation. They had never heard such things. One after the other threw away his bone, wiped his mouth and made himself comfortable by the fire.

When he spoke of the angels, one ofthe listeners said, "Doesn't God stand by the angels and the devil by man? A magician taught me this. God cast us out of Paradise and placed us into the domain of the devil. We serve him the way it suits us."

Enoch continued, "Man stands between God and the devil like the flower between light and darkness. With its blossom, it opens to the light and with its roots it takes hold of the darkness and holds itself upright!" With powerful words Enoch praised the beings and the workings of the Light, so that one after the other of the robber band wiped away the jagged black lines. They had hardly noticed how the fire had died down. When one of the men put wood on the fire and the flame flared up, all the men turned their clean brows toward the fire. Enoch rose, reached into his coat-pocket and threw fragrant resin into the flame. Then he spoke the words of the holy sacrifice.

When they witnessed the holy sacrifice and thought about their misdeeds, tears of shame and remorse flowed from the eyes of the men. They begged Enoch, "Let us go with you. We no longer want to stay in our robber-caves." The next morning, they bathed in the river to cleanse themselves. From then on, Enoch always went forth with a band of companions. From day to day his following band grew until it was a whole tribe. Then he decided to stay in one place. He chose a place at the foot of a mountain near to the cave where Adam's Book was hidden. From that time onward, he lived in the cave. His followers built houses all around and worked the land. They were happy to be able to live near Enoch.

The Mountain of God and Its Priests

Ever more people came to hear Enoch's words. He went to the hill above his cave each day to make a sacrifice at the altar and to speak to the people about the realm of heaven. Great throngs of people set up tents on the hillside. Enoch's words filled them with the warmth and the light of God. They lived in peace as brothers and sisters. It is said that in Enoch's time the fields yielded more grain and the trees bore fruit in greater abundance. Evil began to leave the hearts of men. Angels brought good news of the earth unto heaven. But Enoch thought, "I will not remain on the earth forever. Men must learn to see the light of God without me. Henceforth, I will make a sacrifice on the mountain only every second day." Gradually Enoch taught men to live in the Light of God without him. He gave them prayers for morning and evening, for work and for rest.

Enoch's Ascension into Heaven

After a year had run its course, Enoch came to the people only every third day. As the years passed, he came less and less often, until he came only on the seventh day of each week. There were many other priests who, as the 'Sons of Seth,' guided mankind, but their sacrifices did not have the power of Enoch's.

Then the time came when Enoch appeared only once every month. On those days, an enormous crowd of people gathered, to honor him as a messenger of God. When his tall figure, clad in white, stood and ministered at the altar on the mountain top, silence fell upon the throng. When he raised his voice to speak the holy words, the mountain winds carried it far into the valley. There was not one who did not go home a better man or woman.

The time came when Enoch appeared only once every year. After seven years had passed, he told his people that he would be leaving them forever. "A call has come to me that I will ascend to heaven. For the last time I say to you, practice and fulfill those deeds on earth that lead to the light of heaven."

The multitude could not understand his words, and many thought he had given them a parable. But lo and behold! When the sacrifice was completed, he did not go toward his cave as usual, but toward a high mountain range whose summit was covered with ice and snow! When the people understood that Enoch was really leaving them forever, a long procession followed him.

After a time, he turned and said, "Go to your homes, good people! Even as I leave you, I shall be near you in the sacrifice if you think of me." Many turned back with heavy hearts and tear-filled eyes. Enoch climbed ever higher toward the steep, rocky mountains. At some distance behind him, a group of loyal people who could not bear to be separated from him still followed. Again he turned, and when they reached him, he said, "Go back my faithful friends!

The earth needs your strength, for when Enoch is gone, a mighty darkness will gather. Be warriors of Light!"

After these words, he climbed into the snow and ice of the highest peaks. Nearly all those who followed turned back. An old man, nearly exhausted, sought shelter from the icy winds in the rocky clefts. He saw several people stagger after Enoch onto the glacier. Snow began to fall. In the fiery glow of the sunset, the old man watched as Enoch faded into the white of the mountain. He saw one after the other of the faithful ones sink down into the snow. They were freezing to death. The red glow of evening faded and stars appeared. All at once, a white winged horse floated to earth from a shining cloud. Like a powerful youth, Enoch mounted the horse. He waved and stretched out his hand to his dying followers. And lo! from the icy grave, the souls, twelve in number, rose upward toward him and clung to the tail of the winged horse! With mighty movements of its wings, the horse soared heavenward and disappeared among the stars.

The next day several men climbed up to the heights to look for their missing companions. On the glacier they found several blocks of ice which they thought to be the bodies of their friends. In the cracks of the rocks, they found only the weak, old man. They carried him on their shoulders down into the valley. When he grew stronger, he told of Enoch's ascension into heaven. Henceforth, he wandered from place to place speaking of what he had seen, so that all who loved Enoch might know how he had been taken up into heaven.

Noah's Ark

Old Methusala

It was evening, and the age-old Methusala was sitting in front of his hut. Lamech, his son, came to him and said, "Dear Father, I have brought you fruit of the field: dates, apples and pears. May they refresh you!"

"Sit by my side, Lamech, that the time may pass more quickly. My feet have grown so old and weak that today they will not carry me. Tell me the news. How do men live in the valley?"

Lamech began to report. "As I was working in the field today, a group of young people came by. They mocked me and my work and threw stones into the field. I turned and walked away, but they aimed their stones at the trees in order to hit the fruit. Look, many of the figs and pears are damaged."

"O, this sinful race!" Methusala said. "What more must my old eyes behold? There was a time when they looked up to Enoch. He went before us up the mountain, and when he offered sacrifices, angels bent down from heaven and blessed all those who prayed. O, Lamech, how dark the world has grown."

"Yes, Father, it is so. People think so much evil. From the huts in the valley come bands of wild men. They roam the countryside, plunder the fields and slaughter the farmers' animals in order to eat them. They have built many stone houses which they call a city. They want a king. The very worst among them, who is feared by everyone, placed a crown upon his own head. A wanderer who saw it all told me this today."

While Lamech spoke, Methusala had been eating of the fruit. Looking at a damaged apple, he said, "Men do not walk the path of God. The world has become corrupt. Even the fruit does not taste as it once did. The grain in the fields is shrivelled and thin. If a new Enoch does not come, the earth will fall totally into sin."

Where Is the House of the Righteous?

In heaven God chose a strong soul and said, "You shall go to earth where your name shall be Noah. On the earth, try to lead men toward the Good. I will be with you." Then God called the angel of birth and said, "Lead this soul into a house on earth wherein the good still shines. This soul shall renew my ways on earth." And the angel of birth searched for a home into which he might lead the soul. Unseen by men, he visited many homes. But wherever he went, darkness, falsehood, lies and hardness of heart greeted him. He thought he would have to return to heaven and report to God Father that on earth there was no home for a good soul.

As he passed the mountains, he saw a house from which peace and goodness shone. When he entered the house, he heard Methusala speaking to Lamech and his wife of the time of Enoch. "Yes, so it was: every evening, on many mountains, the fires of sacrifice burned. People turned to God in thankfulness for the blessings of fruit, grain, and water. At that time, the kernels of grain were juicy and sweet, not so hard and dry as they are today. The earth rejoiced in giving good nourishment to men, since they walked the paths of Light."

For a long time the angel listened to Methusala. He saw how his words brought light to Lamech's soul and how his wife sat listening in silent devotion. Then the angel of birth knew, "In this house, Noah's soul may become a child." He returned to heaven and reported all he had learned on his journey over the earth. Lamech's house was a house of righteousness.

Noah's Birth

One day, some time later, as Lamech was returning from the field, he saw a large flock of white doves encircling his house. The doves flew in larger and ever larger circles over the roof. The sight was so wonderful that Lamech stood in awe and watched their flight. A maid hurried from the house to the field. "Lamech come home! Your wife has given birth to a son!"

When Lamech neared the house, the bright, circling flock of doves was still there. When he entered the house, he found it radiant with light. He looked at his son and took him up in his arms. Lamech knew that a strong, heavenly soul had come to live in this child. The old Methusala lifted his eyes toward heaven and said, "His name shall be Noah. Through him the earth will be saved from corruption."

The Child Noah's Anger

Noah grew up in the quiet house on the hillside. Ancient Methusala told him of earlier, holier times. They were sitting in front of the hut one day and looked down into the valley. Young Noah asked, "Look at the dark smoke rising from the valley. It is spreading like a dusky dragon over the land."

Methusala answered, "It comes from the sinful city, where idols are worshipped."

Noah asked, "What is idol-worship?"

Methusala replied, "You know, Noah, how God created our beautiful world. To Him we bring offerings of thanks, as the first people on earth did. But the spirits of darkness want to turn men away from God. At night when men sleep, the demons bring evil thoughts into them. Then people no longer want to serve God. Instead they build images of the evil spirits and worship them."

When Methusala finished, anger flared up in Noah's eyes. He clenched his fists and shouted, "When I am grown, I will go into the city and destroy the idols!"

One day, Noah was playing at the brook. He had dug many little canals in the meadow and was letting water flow through them. As he was playing, several young ruffians came from the direction of the city. They carried sacks on their backs, filled with stolen fruit. They called and coaxed the sheep, grazing on the meadow where Noah was playing. When the trusting creatures came, the boys began to throw stones at them. The stricken sheep bleated loudly in pain and fled to their shepherd, Noah. The ruffians put down their sacks and came up to Noah who stood among his sheep. The group of boys had evil in their minds and wanted to have their fun. With a long stick, the foremost fellow struck the frightened animals.

Like a lion, Noah leaped on the fellow, seized him, and with enormous strength threw him into the brook! Howling and dripping wet, he crawled out. Two others tried to take hold of Noah, but each in turn landed in the water. Meanwhile, the rest of the cowardly band had picked up their sacks and run. Noah returned to his sheep. His whole body shook. Tears stood in his eyes. He threw himself onto the ground and sobbed. He, who could not harm even a bug, had thrown himself upon children and fought against them. The sheep calmed down after a time and lay down by their good shepherd. The brook babbled as before, and Noah's tears dried.

In the evening Noah told Methusala and Lamech what had happened that day. They were both amazed that the boy had grown so strong. Methusala said, "Do not fear those bad fellows from the city. Protect the weak. Be brave against evil, and God will always be with you."

The City of a Hundred Idols

Many years passed and Noah grew to manhood. Old Methusala said to Noah one day, "Last night I dreamed that we should go into the city. Tomorrow let us go together into the city of the idol-worshippers."

"Very well," said Noah. "Perhaps we shall succeed in preventing some people from doing evil!" The next day they went into the city, which they had never before visited.

The watchman at the gate greeted them, "Why do you two act so devout and solemn? Can't you be joyful when you enter our city?" With a sneer, he spilled the last of his wine over them.

Methusala whispered, "Be calm, Noah. It is not yet time to oppose them!" They went on into the city. Everywhere they looked, they saw men and women standing lazily about. No one worked. Men were fighting over stolen goods. Children were throwing stones at an old man, while men and women stood by and applauded when the stones struck him.

Noah could hold back his anger no longer. Shielding the old man with his cloak, he shouted, "You cowards! Have you forgotten that your hands were given to you by God for work and prayer?"

Jeering laughter greeted him, yet his bold words and deeds impressed the people, and no more stones were thrown. Noah said to the old man, "Follow me if you want to leave the city!"

The old man answered, "You have saved my life. They would have stoned me until I lay bleeding in the dust. They often do this for sport or to pass time." The old man followed his protector.

As they went on, they passed a house from which came the pitiful weeping and whimpering of children. Noah entered the house and found four wretched children. The eldest said, "Our father and mother were killed in a brawl. We have no food, and this evening we must leave our hut. Two men were here who wanted to drive us out. They said that if we are still here this evening, they will beat us and throw us into the street."

"Come with me, children," said Noah. "I will give you food and shelter." He took the youngest child into his arms, and the other three followed behind.

Soon after, Noah and Methusala came to a great square where a circle of people had assembled. From the distance they could see a fire flaming high. Men with blackened faces were dancing around it. Noah asked one of the crowd what was happening. He answered, "We are burning those men and women who have dared to speak against our king."

Noah asked, "What have they said against the king?"

The man answered, "One of them said, 'The king should see to it that the people work. There should not be so much idleness.' A woman dared to say that the king would do better to provide for the sick instead of carrying on war-games! Those who criticize the king are killed."

Then Noah asked, "Who are the dancers with the blackened faces?"

"Those are the king's servants. They are at his side day and night, in order to protect him and carry out his commands. Now they are dancing around the stone image, which all who come here must worship."

Then Methusala whispered to Noah, "Come, let us go home. We have seen enough evil for one day." Together with the children and the old man, they left the city.

Noah's heart was deeply saddened by all that he had learned. He said to Methusala, "Never will I take a wife and raise children if such corruption awaits them." Noah did not go back into the city. The children grew up to be faithful servants of his house and the old man became a good shepherd.

The Command

One night Noah awoke to the call of his name. He raised his head from his bed and listened. Again a voice called, "Noah, do you hear Me?"

Then Noah knew that it was not a human voice, but the voice of God that called him. He answered, "Yes, Lord, I hear."

The voice continued, "Noah, the evil and sin of men rise up to Me like dull, heavy smoke. Say to all who can hear, 'Refrain from evil! Leave off your misdeeds, or God will send a punishment that will be your destruction.' Tell this to all mankind. Cry it out to them!"

When Noah saw old Methusala the next day, he told him of the revelation. How surprised he was when Methusala told him that he had heard the very same words! Again they prepared to go into the villages and cities in order to fulfill God's command and admonish the people.

At this time, also at God's command, Noah took a wife, whose name was Namoa. The Lord said, "From your family, good men shall people the earth." Namoa bore three sons, whose names were Sem, Ham and Jafet.

The King with the Black Crown

Noah and Methusala journeyed far and called upon all people to walk the path of God, but they found little hearing. They came a second time to the City of a Hundred Idols. This time no watchman stood at the gate. Great multitudes crowded into the city on that day to see the king hold court. Once a week the king held court in order to punish those who vexed him.

From a distance, Noah could see the king in the square, where the court was being held. At his side stood an idol. The king wore a black crown and a blood-red gown. A number of men were kneeling before him on the stony ground. They bowed their heads before the king and the idol, until their foreheads touched the ground.

Suddenly the king pointed his sword at the kneeling men. Immediately executioners jumped forward and cut off their heads, which rolled to the foot of the throne. At the same time, wildly dancing men thumped upon drums, creating a dreadful noise. More prisoners were brought before the king.

Noah forced his way through the mass of people toward the king with the black crown. Boldly he placed himself before the idol and called with a booming voice, "Hold! Stop! You sinful people, what are you doing? I stand before you as a messenger of God and proclaim: Leave off worshipping your devils' faces. Leave off your demonic ways. Kneel down before God, who makes the sun go round the heavens and the stars rise and set." He seized a hammer from one of the drummers and began to smash the stone image with such powerful strokes that the pieces flew in all directions!

Shouting loudly, the king commanded his servants to lay hold of the offender and kill him. Like wild animals they advanced toward Noah. Slowly Noah lowered the hammer and stood quietly gazing before him. The menacing servants stretched out their hands to seize him but suddenly withdrew with tearful cries. Noah was enveloped by a glow of light, whose brightness and warmth burned them when they tried to lay hold of him. Pale as death, the king stepped down from his throne and mounted his black steed. In his haste, his crown fell from his head and rolled onto the ground. In terror, he galloped away.

Great excitement came over the masses of people. Many ran away from the place, shouting and screaming. Others stood rooted to the spot, eager to see how this drama would end. When the tumult subsided, Noah continued, "Leave off worshipping idols. Worship

God, who has created the heavens and the earth." But their hearts had become so hardened by evil that they were unwilling to listen. They turned away and left the square. No one, however, dared to come near Noah.

A small group of people had taken Noah's words into their hearts. They came toward him and said, "Master, your words are good. What shall we do?"

Noah answered, "Follow me out of the city, for God will destroy it." Thus Methusala and Noah left the city followed by a small band of people whose hearts still had a spark of goodness. Outside the city gates, a few turned back, not ready to leave off their sinful ways. The rest of them followed behind Noah and Methusala.

Raphael Guides Noah to the Book of Life

After visiting the city, Noah's soul was deeply troubled. The Archangel Raphael appeared to him and said, "I have come to you at God's command to help heal the earth." He helped Noah to understand the acts of life and the meaning of death, to distinguish between good and evil spirits. Raphael took Noah to the cave of the Holy Book, which Adam had once passed on to Seth, and Seth had passed on to Enoch. It was now revealed to Noah.

What did he find in the wisdom of the Holy Book? He learned to heal many sicknesses. He learned to understand the powers of the sun, moon, and stars. He was able to fathom the past events of the earth, the present, and the future.

The Commandment to Build the Ark

When Noah's soul was filled with the holiness of the Book, God Himself spoke to him and said, "Noah, I have decided to destroy the sinful race of men on earth! Great rains will fall and flood waters will rise. For forty days and forty nights the wells of the heavens and the depths will break open. Water will cover the land and the mountains of the old world. But you, Noah, together with your family, shall be saved and brought to a new world. Build a large chest of cedar wood. Build chambers therein, and seal the cracks with pitch. High up, make a window, and on one side, make a door. The chest should have three floors: one in the bottom, one in the middle and one high-up. Bring all the animals of the earth into the chest, two of each kind. Take food in plenty with you. When the time has come, go into the chest with your three sons and your household that you may be saved for a new world."

When God had spoken thus, Noah called his sons Sem, Ham and Jafet and told them what God had commanded. They rejoiced greatly that they could serve God by building an Ark.

With all the men of the family, they set out to a nearby mountain called Cardinon. They felled the giant cedars growing there. When they had finished joining the first beams and boards, old Methusala died. Before his soul departed from his body he said, "Now I may die in peace and comfort, for I have seen the building of a Temple for a new and better world." With the temple he meant the Ark, which was built according to the measurements God had given to Noah.

Sem, Ham, Jafet, and the Animals

Before the command to build the Ark, Sem often followed after the birds, for he loved them dearly. He found the nests of the eagles on the mountain crags and observed how the young eaglets learned to fly. One day he brought home an eaglet. He tamed it. When the eaglet was fully grown, it always returned to Sem after soaring over the mountains. Sem learned the whistle of every bird in the forest. He coaxed the cuckoo, the woodpecker, and the many songbirds to come to him. They pecked seeds from his hands. A wild dove often perched upon his shoulder.

Ham was a courageous fellow, of mighty strength. He tamed wild animals, above all, the lions. As he was walking through a clump of trees one day, a lion sprang at him. With lightning speed, Ham stepped aside and the lion struck a tree trunk! Ham leaped onto the lion, knelt upon him, and grasped his neck. He pressed the lion's throat so firmly that the beast gasped for air. Gradually he let the lion breathe. This lion became so tame that he followed Ham like a faithful dog. From then on, Ham was never seen without his lion.

Jafet loved the shepherd's life. He brought the sheep and cattle to pasture and watched over them. He tamed a powerul bull, which now pulled his plow over the fields.

Will the Ark Be Destroyed?

The people in the City of a Hundred Idols had seen that something unusual was happening on Mount Cardinon. But no one knew what was being built. Some people mocked, "Noah is building a huge coffin. He and his family want to bury themselves alive!"

Five men decided, "Whatever it is, it would be a devilish joy to burn up the big crate." One evening an overly bold group made its way up the mountain to do just that. The leader carried a clay pot full of glowing embers. Others carried dry wood and straw. The men did not know, however, that Ham always left his lion under the Ark in order to protect it at nighttime. Noah had feared that unkind people from the city might try to do harm. Sem's eagle made his nightly resting place on the top-most beam of the Ark. Of this the men were also unaware.

Silently, five shadowy figures crept toward the Ark. From time to time they stopped to listen. They heard nothing. Both the lion and the eagle slept. Inside the Ark, together with the workmen, Sem, Ham, and Jafet slept on a bed of straw. The five men hid behind a bush. There was a slight rustling of leaves. A thin wisp of smoke rose from the pot of embers, which a gentle breeze blew toward the Ark. Half asleep, the lion stroked his nose with his paw and sneezed. A few more steps and the coals could be poured under the dry timbers. Already the leader was lifting the coals out of the pot. A bundle of straw was aflame!

All at once there was a mighty roar. The lion leaped into the middle of the flames and seized the fire-setter. The other men fled in terror. The eagle rose from his perch and, with a loud cry, flew after the fleeing men. He scratched their faces and pecked their shoulders so that they cried out in pain. They thought an awful monster was pursuing them.

In the Ark, Sem, Ham, and Jafet jumped up in alarm. They heard the tumult and smelled the smoke. When they looked under the Ark, they saw the glowing coals and quickly smothered them with sand. Then they found the lion, with his forepaw upon the evil man's chest. When Noah came, he patted the lion and thanked God that the Ark was unharmed. From then on, the three brothers took turns guarding the Ark during the night.

Gathering the Animals

When the Ark was completed and all the cracks filled in with pitch, Noah said to his youngest son, "You, Jafet, are friend of the larger animals, the cow, the bull, and all those that crawl upon the earth. Go, and bring a pair of each of them. Build a large corral with a strong fence and gather the animals within it. Later we will lead them into the Ark. They shall find room in the lowest chamber of the Ark."

Jafet asked, "How shall I know which animals to choose?"

Noah answered, "God has given me a sign that angels will help us choose and guide the animals. Take all those along which peacefully lie down before you when you come near." Thus Jafet set out to gather the larger animals.

To Sem, Noah said, "You are friend of the eagle and the birds. Gather a pair of each kind. They may roost in the trees of a nearby forest until we are ready to let them fly into the uppermost chambers of the Ark."

Sem said, "Father, what shall give us light in the Ark, since we must close all the windows?"

Noah answered, "Go into the mountains. In a cave, you will find the wondrous Anoa stone; this precious stone will give us light in the Ark."

Sem set out toward the mountains, coaxing and calling the birds. One evening he chanced upon a cave from which a mysterious light shone. Here he found the precious Anoa stone. He carried it in his hand like a crystal. When he returned into the valley, a great swarm of birds circled over his head and followed him. When he sat down to rest, the birds perched in the trees. When he went on his way, the birds rose into the air and flew in the direction of the Ark. Only the snowhens and partridges cackled as they ran along the ground behind him. In this way, Sem returned to the forest near the Ark. The birds roosted in the trees. They whistled and sang the whole day. No large bird, however, harmed a smaller one. They all sat happily together and sang in the branches of the trees, as long ago they did in the Garden of Eden.

Entering the Ark

The Ark was finished and all the cracks were sealed. Sem, Ham, and Jafet went to Noah and said, "Tell us, Father, how we shall bring the animals into the Ark, for all is ready."

Noah commanded, "First, bring food into the Ark. Although the animals will sleep through most of our long journey, they will need food. Then you, Jafet, bring the heaviest animals into the lowest chamber. You, Ham, bring yours into the middle. When all are within, open the roof-window for Sem, so that the birds may enter."

Then Noah's sons and the other members of his family brought many kinds of food into the Ark. Above all, they brought grains, figs, ivy leaves, and fruit. Noah himself brought grape vines, figs, and olive trees. These he wanted to plant in the new world.

After all this was done, it was time for Jafet to lead his animals into the Ark. Wide beams were placed to make a bridge. First Jafet led the bull, the cow, and the other domestic animals. He had brought only young elephants, buffalo and giraffes, for the door was too small for fully grown creatures.

There was much squirming on the bridge when the creeping animals, such as snakes, salamanders, and lizards crawled into the Ark. One thing was unusual: no animal harmed another! They lived in peace and friendship as they once had done in Paradise. The snake forgot that she had a poisonous fang. Even the porcupines and hedgehogs tried to keep their bristles smooth. The lowest chamber was filled. The animals lay down and soon fell into a deep slumber.

Now Ham led the lions, panthers, leopards, wildcats and a train of other forest animals into the Ark. They, too, lay down quietly in their chambers in the middle section.

Then Noah opened the roof-window, and Sem whistled to the birds. They came in pairs as he called them. Had they come all at once, they would have crushed and broken their wings!

When the sun went down, Noah said, "For today, let us close the Ark. Tomorrow, my sons, you must go on a journey with me. I have been commanded to bring Adam's casket into the new world."

Just as Noah was about to close the door, something fluttered around his head. Two bats squeaked fearfully and begged to be let in. "Aha," Noah said, "You did not know whether you belonged with the mice or the birds. Come in!" At these words two night-owls appeared. "Hm," said Noah, "You are afraid the other birds will ruffle your feathers if you sit by them. Sit on my shoulders." The owls happily perched on Noah's shoulders, while the bats held fast to his arm.

He climbed up to the birds' chamber. Most of them were already sleeping. He brought the night creatures into a corner. "Finally I can close the door," said Noah. But, lo and behold, the snails had crept up the door frame and were stuck there. They had only just arrived. Noah took them down to the lowest chamber. Then he locked the door.

Adam's Casket

One last time Noah and his sons left the Ark, to go to the cave where Adam's body was entombed. Led by an angel, they found the place, a grotto under the earth. Filled with awe and reverence, the three brothers lifted the casket upon their shoulders and bore it to the Ark, just as Noah had bidden them. Onto the casket they fastened the precious Anoa stone, which spread a dim light through the darkness of the Ark.

When everything had been brought into the Ark, Noah prayed to God and said, "Lord, we have fulfilled the work as You have commanded. Be with us according to Your Will."

The Ark Is Sealed and the Rain Begins to Fall

All who had helped to build the Ark entered it: Noah's sons, their wives, and all their families. Standing in the doorway, Noah cast a parting look at the old world, as if he expected someone else to come. His eye scanned the horizon, but no one appeared. Slowly, he closed the heavy door.

Soon thereafter a white cloud neared the Ark. A hand stretched forth from the cloud and wrote a sign upon the door that it should remain locked until another sign was given.

The Flood

For many days, dark clouds had been billowing landward. A mysterious, terrifying thunder rolled from far and near. Suddenly rain began to pour from the sky with such force that people sought shelter in houses and caves and under trees. They cursed terribly, shook their fists against heaven and cried, "Do you want to drown us down here?" When the rain did not stop falling during the night, however, and the water ran into houses and huts, a terrible fear came over them. At first they climbed to the upper parts of the houses and into the trees. Many began making small rafts out of beams and boards.

But the rain kept falling and the water rose higher and higher. Between the lightning flashes and rumbling thunder, the cries and wails of people could be heard. Those who were able to flee hurried to the mountains. Many hungry hoards gathered there incuding the sinful king and his followers.

When the rain let up for a short time, and a ray of light broke through the clouds, they could see the Ark floating by. Driven by the wind, it passed close by the sinking City of a Hundred Idols. Loud shouts resounded. "Noah, Noah, save us! We will heed your words. Save us!" But their repentance was too late. The winds swallowed up their pleas and cries.

Several good swimmers swam to the Ark. When they reached it, they held fast to the cracks. With their fists they struck the sides of the Ark, shouting, "Noah, open up!" But their voices did not penetrate the wood, and their thumping was like the soft, dull tread of the animals on the wooden floor.

At this hour, Noah gathered his family for a prayer of thanks. He said, "My heart is heavy and my eyes are full of tears because a terrible judgment has been passed upon sinful men. May God have pity on their souls, since He must destroy their bodies."

The next day a mighty storm arose, and the Ark was cast about by enormous flood waves. A terrible earthquake shook the old world. Mountains and lands sank. The rafts split asunder and the clinging survivors were cast into the rolling waves. On the mountains the remaining people huddled together. Many jumped into the water in desperation. On the tip of the highest mountain sat the King of Sin. He had clothed himself in a tiger-skin. In his right hand, he held a sword. Before him stood his servants, from whose faces the rain had washed off the sooty signs.

When the water rose to the highest peak, these evil people pushed into the water all those who tried to clamber upward. Hastily they carried stones, in order to build up the mountain peak a little higher. When evening fell, the servants huddled around the feet of their king. He shouted at them to jump into the water. He brandished his sword, until one after the other disappeared in the flood. The last one to remain, however, struggled and fought the king to the end. He wrenched the bloody sword from the king and cast it into the water. Not long thereafter, the black crown followed. They fought on. The water rose to their knees. Suddenly, entangled in each others arms, they lost their footing and silently slipped into the rolling waves. The last human bodies of the old world sank into the depths of the ocean.

Distress in the Ark

When the earth quaked during the fierce storm, and enormous waves whipped the water, Noah and his family were in great distress. Animals and people lost their footing and were cast against the walls of the Ark. All the creatures awakened. Loud, fearful moans echoed through the Ark. Only the snails and the groundhogs slept on. The giraffes suffered terribly. Their heads always struck the ceiling. Jafet sawed a hole in the ceiling so they could stick their heads into the middle section. When Ham walked about on the second floor, he bumped against a head and a neck without legs. Only then did he recognize the giraffes' heads which reached into his chamber.

Sem, Ham, and Jafet had much trouble calming the animals. The snakes became terrified, when first a cow and then a donkey stepped on them. Jafet gathered the snakes together in a corner and told them to coil up.

When Ham came to the lion, the lion growled because the wolf had lain down beside him. Ham stroked the lion's mane and pulled the wolf's ear when he bared his fangs. Then both beasts became calm again.

The loudest noises, however, came from above. Cackling, cawing, whistling, and screeching filled the whole birdhouse. Sem fed them grains and seeds; while they were pecking and eating, the birds forgot their distress. When Sem came to the ducks, he saw that throughout the storm they had kept still in their corner. He patted their feathers and spoke a few kindly words. The ducks thought, "The other birds want to ruffle our feathers. Man pets us. He is good."

When the storm calmed, the brothers fed the animals. Soon they all fell into a deep sleep, and they did not awaken until they reached the new world.

Raven-Flight and Dove-Message

A steady wind drove the Ark eastward for more than forty days. Then one day, Sem came from the topmost chamber into the middle and said to Noah, "Father, it is so quiet. Rain is no longer falling. Surely the great rain has passed!" Noah climbed to the top and listened. No rain could be heard. It had stopped!

Noah said, "Give me the ladder. I will open the window and look out." He saw nothing but water, water and dull, foggy clouds.

Sem said, "Let a raven fly out. He can fly far and look around. Maybe he can bring us news." Noah let a raven fly out. The raven circled far and near over the water. Finally, he flew into the distance and did not return. He was the first to find the new world!

Later, Noah let a dove fly out to find land. After several hours the dove returned. She could find no place to rest. Noah locked the window and said, "We must wait patiently for the Lord's command. He will give us a sign."

After seven more days, he let the dove fly out again. In the evening the dove returned. Behold! She had broken off an olive twig and brought it back in her beak! Then Noah knew that the waters on earth had ebbed. But where had the dove found the branch? She had been to the Mount of Olives, where in later times the city of Jerusalem was built and where many other events occurred.

After seven more days, Noah let loose another dove. This dove did not return. Then he was certain that the time was near at hand when he would look upon the new world. But still he waited for a sign from God.

The New World

One day a tremor shook the Ark, as if the Ark had struck something solid. But Noah did not open the door for he knew that the earth had to dry before the animals could be let out. Not long after, God spoke to Noah during the night, "The time is at hand. Leave the Ark and take the animals with you."

The next morning Noah opened the door. The fresh, green world lay before him! He ordered Sem to let the birds out. Sem opened the window and let the eagle out first. What a splendid sight it was as the majestic bird rose into the sunny blue sky! Then thousands of many-colored birds flew after it into the air.

Ham freed the animals of the middle chamber. The lion and his family sprang out with happy leaps. Since the animals were still tame, the paradise-like peace stayed with them for a good while.

Finally Jafet led forth the bull and the other heavy animals. The snakes wriggled and slithered into the bushes. The mice scampered into the nearest holes. The snails, naturally, came last of all; some of them remained stuck to the Ark for several more days.

Noah walked through the Ark to see if all the animals had gone. At the top, he found the owls and the bats in their dark corner. He knew that they wanted to wait for nightfall to fly out, and so he left them in peace.

The Offering of Thanks

With the help of his sons, Noah built an altar of stones beside the Ark. There was not a single member of the family who did not carry stones joyfully for this first altar in the new world. The first fire was lit, a fire of thanks. As the people knelt at the altar and thanked God for saving them from the flood, a magnificent rainbow spanned the sky. In his heart, Noah heard the voice of God saying, "I accept your offering. Nevermore will I send a flood over the earth. Live by My commandments. The rainbow shall be a sign of our covenant."

As Noah heard the words in his heart, he proclaimed them from the altar. Sem said, "I will be a priest of the Lord, that the offering may always be kept holy in the new world."

The Devil in Noah's Vines

On the slopes of Mount Ararat, Noah planted the trees he had brought from the old world: the fig tree, the olive tree, and the almond tree. He also planted the grapevines to have a small vineyard. As he was planting the vines, Satan came to him and asked, "What are you putting into the ground?"

Noah answered, "I am planting a vineyard."

The devil asked, "What will become of the sticks?"

Noah replied, "The fruit of the vine is sweet, when fresh or when dried. From the berries a juice is pressed which delights men."

The devil slinked away. Some days later, when Noah was not there, he returned with a sheep, a lion, an ape, and a pig. He killed the sheep and let its blood flow into the vineyard. Then he killed the lion, the ape, and the pig, and let their blood soak into the earth.

The devil grinned and said, "When men drink the first cup of wine, they will be like the meek lamb. The second cup will make them feel as strong as the lion. They will say, 'I am king: there is no one like me.' With the third cup, they will be drunk and stalk about like apes; then they will not know anymore what to do. Finally, if they drink more wine, they will spill it upon their clothes and roll on the floor like the pigs!" He grinned and thought, "Already I have brought something to the new world which will bring men upon my path."

Sem and the Angels

Noah continued to live in the Ark, but his sons and their families built houses at the foot of Mount Ararat. Sem said to Noah, "Father, an angel of God has bid me to take Adam's casket upon my back and to follow where he leads me. Adam is to have his grave in the new world also."

Noah answered, "My son, fulfill the commandment the angel has given you. I will remain here and make the offerings." Thus Sem took Adam's casket upon his strong shoulders and walked down Mount Ararat into the valley.

The angel walked by his side and led Sem on a long journey to a hill which was later called Golgatha. When Sem came to the hill, the ground opened up before him. He placed Adam's body into the earth. When the earth had received the body of man's ancestor, it closed itself. The angel spoke to Sem, "Through Adam, death came to mankind. In future times, when mankind will become evil again, God will send his Son as a Savior. From this place He will bring life and light to earth."

Then Sem built a hut nearby and from that day onward remained a servant of the great mystery that the angel had revealed to him at Adam's grave.

Afterword

This collection of stories and descriptions is the result of the author's work over a period of years introducing children of the lower grades to the world of the Old Testament. I have drawn from various biblical sources and apocryphal texts, especially Ben Gurion's *Collected Legends of the Jews (Sagen der juden)*. Out of the oral tradition, these stories bring in legendary form a concise, biblical report that is poetically and mythologically accessible for the developing child from age 8–10.

Sympathy with the good, the divine world and sadness and darkness resulting from the expulsion from light make up not only the drama of the Old Testament, but also of the individual human being. It is this which the child experiences and follows, on the wings of his feelings. If one succeeds in letting the reality of nature grow out of the divine, colorful background of a world creation, then awe, reverence, and love of nature can blossom. If sin and corruption as evolutionary forces are transformed into good and then clarified, moral powers are awakened. More powerful, significant pictures than those expressed in the great events of the Old Testament can hardly be found!

The form of these stories has been freely created out of an inner attitude of responsibility toward their sources. It is hoped that they will touch the children's hearts and feelings, as well as be a stimulus in the early lessons dealing with world religions.

– Jakob Streit

Translator's Note

The pedagogical value of these stories prompted me to translate them into English. I have tried to maintain a narrative, conversational tone and style and avoid using latinate words which could create difficulty for children 8–10 years old. The Hebrew was added so that at least the "First Day" might also live in recitation.

– Ekkehard Piening

Editor's Note

This edition is a complete revision of the first edition. Sections have been retranslated, spelling has been modernized, and the format has been made consistent with current standards set by the *Chicago Manual of Style, 14th edition.* Waldorf Publications is grateful to Jakob Streit for permission to reintroduce this valuable book to English-speaking readers.

– David Mitchell

From Genesis

Be RESHIT BARA ELOHIM ET HASHAMAYIM Ve'ET HA'AREZ.

bə'rɛʃi:t	ba:a':	ɛlɔhi':m	ɛt	Haiʃa:má:ji:m	vɔɛ't	ha:a':rɛts
beh-res he'et	ba-ra'	elo he'em	et	hashama'yeem	veh-e't	ha a'rets

Ve HA'AREZ HAYTA TOHU VAVOHU Ve CHOSHECH

və ha:a'rɛts	hajita':	tɔ'hu:	va:vɔ'hu:	vəχɔ'ʃɛχ
ve ha-a'rets	high-ta'	to'who	va vo'whu	ve-cho'shech

AL-PNEY THOM,

a:l-pne'i	təhɔ'm
al-pneigh	te-ho'mm,

VE RUACH ELOHIM: Me RACHEFET AL-PNEY HAMAJIM.

vəru':a:χ	ɛlɔhi:m:	məra:χɛ'fɛt	al-pne'i	ha:má:ji:m
veru'ach	eloheém	me rache'fet	al-pnei'gh	ha ma'yeem

VAYOMER ELOHIM: YeHI'OR VAYHI-'OR.

vaijɔ'mer	ɛlɔhi:'m	jə hi': ɔr	va:jəhi': ɔr
vigh o'mer	eloheém	ye he'e or	vigh he'e or

VAYAR ELOHIM ET HA'OR KI-TOV;

Va:ja:'r	ɛlɔhi':m	ɛt	ha:ɔ'r	ki:tɔ'v;
vigha'r	eloheém	et	ha o'r	kee to'v

VAYAVDEL ELOHIM BEYN HA'OR 'UVEYN HACHOSHECH.

va:ja:v dɛ'l	ɛlɔhi:'m	bein	ha:ɔ'r	u-vei'n	ha:χɔ́'ʃɛχ.
vigh av de'l	eloheém	beighn	ha'o'r	oovei'gn	hachóshech

VAYIKRA ELOHIM LA'OR YOM VeLACHOSHECH KARA

vaji:kra':	ɛlɔhi:'m	la:ɔ'r	jɔ'm	vəla:χɔ'ʃɛχ	ka:ra'
vighikra'	eloheém	la o'r	yom	velacho'shech	kara'

LAYLA, VAYeHI, 'EREV VAYeHI, VOKER, YOM ECHAD.

la':jla:	va:jɛ hi:	ɛrɛ'v	va:jɛ hi':	vɔ'kɛr,	jɔ'm	ɛχa:d,
líghl a	vigh-eh-heé	e'rev	vigh-eh-he'e	vo'ker	yo'm	echád

a	as	in	far	i	as	in	see
ay	as	in	nigh	e	as	in	net
ey	as	in	neigh	ch	as	in	Loch

Other Titles by Jakob Streit Published by Waldorf Publications

www.waldorfpublications.org

Journey to the Promised Land

The Path of the People of Israel from Abraham's Calling to David's Dream

ISBN 1-888365-23-4

165 pages 6 x 9 inches

$15.00

We Will Build a Temple

The Path of Israel from King Solomon to John the Baptist

ISBN 1-888365-55-2

103 pages 6 x 9 inches

$15.00

Puck the Gnome

ISBN 1-888365-23-4

100 pages 6 x 9 inches

$14.00

Liputto

Stories of Gnomes and Trolls

ISBN 1-888365-26-9

58 pages 7 x 11 inches

$15.00

Made in the USA
Coppell, TX
08 June 2020

27072727R00063